The Marshall Cavendish

International

WILDLIFE

ENCYCLOPEDIA

VOLUME 5

CAC – COB

MARSHALL CAVENDISH
NEW YORK · LONDON · TORONTO · SYDNEY

Revised Edition Published 1991

Published by Marshall Cavendish Corporation
2415 Jerusalem Avenue
North Bellmore, NY 11710
USA

Printed and bound in Italy by LEGO Spa Vicenza

Library of Congress Cataloging-in-Publication Data

Marshall Cavendish International wildlife encyclopedia/general
  editors, Maurice Burton and Robert Burton.
    p. cm.
    ''Portions of this work have also been published as The
International wildlife encyclopedia, Encyclopedia of animal life and
Funk & Wagnalls wildlife encyclopedia.''
    Includes index.
    Contents: v. 5. CAC-COB.
    ISBN 0-86307-734-X (set).
    ISBN 0-86307-739-0 (v. 5).
    1. Zoology–Collected works. I. Burton, Maurice, 1898-
II. Burton, Robert, 1941-   . III. Title: International wildlife
encyclopedia.
QL3.M35 1988
591'.03'21–dc 19

Cacomistle

A relative of the raccoon, the cacomistle is slender and sleek, up to 2½ ft long of which 17 in. is bushy tail, ringed black and white, and it weighs only about 2½ lb. The coat is greyish-buff, darker along the back and white on the underparts. The face is fox-like, the eyes are large and ringed with white, contrasting with black patches, and the ears are large and pricked. The feet are well furred, and the claws can be partly withdrawn. It ranges the southwestern US and nearby Mexico.

The original Mexican name is caco-mixtle, meaning rush-cat, and an alternative Mexican name is tepemixtle or bush-cat. In the United States, it has been given a variety of names: ringtail, coon cat, raccoon fox, band-tailed cat, cat-squirrel, mountain cat, ringtailed cat. Its fur is valuable and is marketed as 'civet cat' and 'California mink'.

Related to the cacomistle is the central American cacomistle, or guayonoche, Bassariscus sumichrasti, *about which very little is known. It lives in the forests of southern Mexico and central America.*

Elusive ringtail

Nocturnal and secretive, the cacomistle usually manages to keep out of sight, so it is little known, even to the local residents. It sleeps by day in a den among rocks, in holes in trees or at the base of trees between buttress roots. Agile in moving among trees, it uses its tail as a balancer and also curls it over its back like a squirrel. It does this especially when alarmed, at the same time giving a squirrel-like scolding or barking.

Expert mouser

The cacomistle's food is small rodents and birds, lizards, insects and fruit. It is well known around the fruit farms of California for its habit of eating the fallen fruit. At times a cacomistle will come to live in a house, cottage or cabin and will keep the place free of mice and rats. Prospectors gave it the name of 'miner's cat'. However, the cacomistle is a menace to poultry farmers.

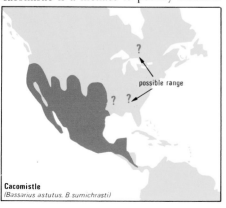

Cacomistle
(Bassarius astutus. B sumichrasti)

possible range
?
? ?

Russ Kinne: Photo Res.

The cacomistle has the large eyes and large ears typical of a night hunter.

Lightweight babies

The gestation period is not known. Births take place in May or June, in a moss-lined nest. The 3 or 4 babies in a litter weigh 1 oz each. They are born blind, with ears closed and the body covered with a downy fur. Some solid food may be taken at 3 weeks. The eyes open at 4 weeks. They are taken hunting at 2 months and are weaned at 4 months. They can live 14 years in captivity.

Night living sunbathers

Animals active by day are termed diurnal, those that come out at night, nocturnal. But even nocturnal animals will sometimes come out during the day, especially to sunbathe.

The European badger, one of the most rigidly nocturnal of animals, will do this at times, and so will the red fox. The cacomistle also sunbathes but it is seldom seen doing so, because it does its basking in the tops of trees, crouched along a branch with its ringed tail dangling over the side, the rest of its body harmonizing with the bark.

class	**Mammalia**
order	**Carnivora**
family	**Procyonidae**
genus & species	***Bassariscus astutus***

Caddis-fly

Caddis-fly is the common name given to the insect order Trichoptera, of which 190 species are known in Britain and between 4 000 and 5 000 throughout the world. Their nearest relatives are the Lepidoptera (butterflies and moths), but caddis wings are hairy instead of scaly. The antennae are long and many-jointed. The adult insects look like moths and fly at night.

Most larvae are aquatic, living in freshwater and breathing by external gills on the sides of the abdominal segments. These are the well-known caddis-worms, which build tubular cases to protect their bodies, although not all caddis-fly larvae do this. All of them spin silk.

Underwater builders

By far the most interesting feature of the caddis-flies is the life of the aquatic larvae, which varies in the different families and genera. They can be divided into two types, those which build portable cases, and are almost all vegetarians, and those which live free and are at least partly carnivorous. The case-builders use many materials in various ways to build their tubes. Members of the genus *Phryganea*, which includes the largest caddis-flies, cut pieces of leaves and stick them together with silk. The most familiar cases are probably those of *Limnophilus*, which are made of small stones, and pieces of plant stems or empty snail shells. If removed from their cases and given beads or similar objects, some of these caddis-flies will use the artificial material to make new ones. *Stenophylax* and *Heliopsyche* use fine sand grains to make their cases, the one a straight cylinder, the other a spiral tube that looks remarkably like a small snail shell. Cases made of stones or sand often have their weight reduced by a bubble of air trapped inside. *Heliopsyche* is American, all the others mentioned are found in Britain.

All the cases are tubular and open at the one end, where the larva pushes out its head and thorax to move about or feed. The rear end is closed with a silken mesh so that a current of water can flow through and aerate the gills. All caddis-larvae have a pair of hooked limbs at the back, used to hold onto the case – so tightly that attempts to pull the larva out invariably injure it. It can easily be made to leave its case, however, by pushing the head of a fairly large pin through the mesh of the rear opening.

Most of the larvae with non-portable cases live in silken tubes, in flowing water, some living under stones in swift upland streams. In the genus *Plectronemia* the larva is nearly 1 in. long and makes a silk tunnel with the open end facing upstream widely flared to form a trumpet-shaped net. Any small animal or piece of plant material carried into this trap by the current is seized and eaten by the larva, which thus gets its food in very much the same way as a web-spinning spider. A number of other stream-dwelling caddis-larvae make nets of various shapes to gather food. When they are damaged, or choked with inedible material, the larvae clean and repair them.

△ *Protective tubular cases, open at one end, are built by caddis-fly larvae from pieces of plant stems and leaves, and small stones and shells, bound together with silk (3 × natural size).*
▽ *The caddis-worm* Lepidostoma hirtum *partly emerges from its tubular case to feed (×16).*

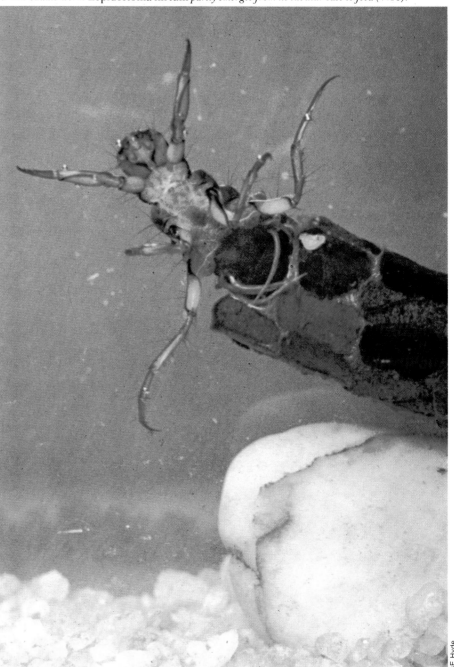

480

Adult feeds on nectar

The mouth-parts of adult caddis-flies are vestigial, and they can take only liquid food. In the wild they probably feed from flowers with exposed nectaries, but will take sugar and water in captivity. Fed in this way they can be kept alive for 2 or 3 months, but given only water they live for less than 2 weeks. The case-bearing larvae eat mainly the leaves and stems of live plants and may be a nuisance when one is trying to establish water lilies in a pond. A cabbage leaf tied to a string, thrown into a pond and left for a few hours, will often be covered with case-bearing caddis-larvae if it is taken out carefully. The large case-bearing larvae of *Phryganea* catch and eat water insects as well as plant food. Most of the tube-dwelling or free-living larvae have a mixed diet.

Life history

The eggs are laid by the females in spring and summer. Some kinds drop them on the surface as they are flying over, others crawl underwater and stick them to stones or plants in a jelly-like mass. Some of the larvae do not make cases or tubes until they have moulted their skins several times, others make tiny cases as soon as they hatch. When the larva is fully grown, nearly a year later, it pupates, inside the case if it belongs to a case-bearing species, otherwise in a silken cocoon. When the time comes for the adult insect to emerge, the pupa bites its way out of the case, being equipped for the purpose with strong mandibles, and swims to the surface of the water. There it splits open, releasing the adult caddis-fly, which can fly almost immediately on emergence. The life history usually takes a year to complete, of which the adult life is only a small fraction.

Anglers and caddis-flies

These insects are of interest to anglers for two reasons. The larvae, taken out of their cases, make excellent bait for the man who watches a float. The adults, when they hatch in quantity, cause a 'rise' of trout, that is to say the fish are stimulated to come to the surface and feed, and this is of prime interest to the fly fishermen.

Entomologists always speak of caddis-flies by their Latin names, but anglers use an English terminology that is hardly ever heard except in the context of fly fishing. They are known collectively as sedge flies, the large *Phryganea grandis* being the great red sedge or murragh. There is a group of species called silverhorns, and some have names of their own such as Grannom, Caperer and Halford's Welshman's Button.

Artificial flies are made in imitation of caddis-flies. To make a murragh a piece of dark grey-black or black-claret mohair or seal's fur is used for the body, a dark brown-speckled feather from a fowl's wing is used for the wings and two dark red cock hackles (the feathers from the neck) complete the job; only the soft fibres near the base of the feather being used.

phylum	Arthropoda
class	Insecta
order	Trichoptera

PH Ward

△ *Adult caddis-fly* Stenophylax permistus *has large wings and flies mainly at night. The adult is short-lived, for only a fraction of the annual life cycle (3 × natural size).*
▽ *Caddis-fly head magnified about 20 times. The compound eye's many facets can be clearly seen.*

NA Callow NHPA

481

Caecilian

The caecilian is a limbless amphibian with a long cylindrical body marked with rings, living wholly underground. The 158 species are worm-like or snake-like according to size, the smallest caecilian being only 4½ in. long, the largest, 4½ ft. Their colour is usually blackish out may be pale flesh-colour. The skin is smooth and slimy, but unlike that of other amphibians, it has small scales embedded in it, in most species. The eyes are quite small, covered over with skin, and usually use-less. There is a peculiar organ of smell; a tentacle on each side of the head lies in a groove running from eyes to tip of snout. Presumably it is protruded when the animal is moving about in its burrow.

As in snakes, one lung is large and long, the other is reduced to a small lobe.

Caecilians live in warm regions, in America from Mexico to northern Argentina, in southern and south-east Asia and in the Seychelles and parts of Africa.

species, also eats small burrowing snakes. They themselves are eaten by certain large burrowing snakes.

Life history

There is no difference between male and female externally. Fertilisation is internal and some species lays eggs, others bear live young.

More is known of the life history of the 15 in. sticky caecilian, the female of which lays some two dozen eggs, each about 1/4 in. in diameter, connected in a jelly-like string. They are laid in a burrow near water, the female coiling her body around the egg-mass until they hatch. The larvae, which escape to water, have a breathing pore on either side of the head. This leads into internal gills, connected with the throat, as in fishes. External gills, present in the embryo, are lost before hatching. They have normal eyes, a flattened tail for swimming, and a head like a newt. At the end of its larval life the breathing pores close, lungs are developed and the young caecilian lives permanently on land, burrowing underground.

The aquatic species of caecilian have sometimes been observed swimming in an eel-like fashion.

regarded as rare animals, although it is now known that they are plentiful enough in suitable habitats. Yet, as with all animals living wholly underground, it is hard to find out anything about their way of life. What we can do, however, is study how they are made, and this is important, because it tells us that caecilians are a link with the large extinct amphibians that lived nearly 400 million years ago, whose footprints are known from the Devonian rocks and their skeletons from the rocks of the next geological period, the Carboniferous (Coal Age). After that there is no trace of them, so they seem to have died out 300 million years ago. Some were crocodile-like, lived on land in the marshes where the coal measures were laid down, and they started life as aquatic larvae. They seemed to have been the first backboned animals to live permanently on land, and they almost certainly evolved from air-breathing fishes, the lobe-finned fishes which were the ancestors of the amphibians.

These ancient amphibians gave rise not only to the present-day amphibians but also to the reptiles. They link, therefore, the fishes, amphibians and reptiles, and the caecilians seem to be their direct surviving descendants. This relationship is seen not

Feeding habits of many caecilians are still unknown, but earthworms are probably important in their diet, as in this species Siphonops annulatus

Ancient burrower
Caecilians are the sole surviving relatives of the earliest land animals, large fossil amphibians which roamed the earth 400 million years ago. Burrows are made in soft earth, and caecilians seldom come above ground except when heavy rain floods the burrows. A number of species are aquatic, and a few species live in leaf litter which is found on the floor of rain forests.

Feeding
Little is known for certain but earthworms are probably the main diet for most species, and a few may eat termites. The sticky caecilian, of southeast Asia, the best-known

Three-way links

The first mention of a caecilian was by Seba, in 1735, which he described as a snake. Linnaeus, in 1754, also included it among the snakes. In 1811, Oppel put caecilians with frogs, toads and salamanders, as amphibians, but these were still regarded as reptiles, even as late as 1859. Then came a change, and the caecilians were thought to be degenerate salamanders. From 1908 on there followed studies of the anatomy, and it gradually became clear that caecilians provided an interesting link with the past.

Even now our knowledge of the caecilians is not extensive. They have always been

only in the degenerate scales found in the caecilian skin but also in the caecilian skull being so like that of these giant amphibians of 400 million years ago. It will be interesting to see if any fossil caecilians are found in the future and to compare them with the present day order. As yet no fossil caecilians have been found.

class	**Amphibia**
order	**Gymnophiona**
family	**Caeciliidae**
genera	***Caecilia, Typhlonectes, Ichthyophis,** others*

PH Ward

Young caiman showing its many, pointed teeth.

Caiman

The several species of caiman are confined to the northern part of South America, mainly in the Amazon basin, and one of the species extends into the southern part of Mexico. They are closely related to alligators, differing mainly in having the skin of the underside reinforced with bony plates. This makes them useless for the leather market, for which crocodiles and alligators have been killed in large numbers, because it is the skin of the belly that is tanned, as well as the sides. Otherwise, in appearance and in habits, caimans and alligators are very much alike. The smallest is the dwarf caiman, up to 4 ft long, the largest is the black caiman, up to 15 ft long.

The five species can be grouped as the spectacled caiman, plus the broad snouted caiman, two smooth-fronted caimans and the black caiman (one species only). Spectacled and broad snouted caimans have a ridge across the nose, between the eyes, like the bridge of a pair of spectacles. Smooth-fronted species lack this. The black caiman also has a smooth forehead but is glossy black in colour, contrasting with the sombre browns and olive of other species.

Belligerent and agile

Caimans can often be seen sunning themselves in great numbers on river banks or in muddy streams in dense jungle. They move with surprising speed over a short distance on land, and are even more agile in water, being quicker and more active than alligators. Those who have kept caimans in captivity claim they are more vicious and ready to bite than alligators or crocodiles, and there are many reports of attacks on human beings. Apart from the possibility of

Caimans differ from crocodiles and alligators in having very large overlapping bony plates on their bellies. They move with surprising speed over a short distance on land, and are even more agile in water, being quicker than alligators.

accidental encounters there are no substantiated reports of deliberate attacks. They are said, however, to kill many domestic animals and when, in some parts of their range, they congregate in small pools during the dry season (November–December) they are killed in great numbers by cowboys.

Caimans readily show fight. Young caimans will blow themselves up, leap about and hiss, with the mouth open ready to bite. Older ones also hiss, and in the breeding season they bellow loudly.

Kills its prey by drowning

Prey is sometimes seized on land and carried back to water to be held under until drowned. A stratagem used for catching a water bird or a mammal coming down to drink is for the caiman to turn and move away, submerge and then swim round to capture it. When swallowing, a caiman stretches its neck out of water, manoeuvring its victim to a head foremost position in the mouth. The hind foot is used for scratching, for rubbing the eyes and to tear the food.

As with most crocodilians, they feed on freshwater crustaceans when small, graduating to amphibians, fish, reptiles, birds and mammals as they mature. An exception is the Paraguayan caiman which seems to live largely on giant snails.

Enemies

Little is known about enemies of the caiman. The jaguar is said to kill young or half-grown caimans, and they have been found in the stomachs of anacondas. Man often kills them.

Fifty eggs in a nest

After mating, the female builds near water, a nest of vegetation and mud scraped together in a mound, which she consolidates by crawling over it. Then she digs a hole in the top and may lay up to 50 eggs in it, the size of a hen's or a goose's egg, according to the species and size. These are hard-shelled and the baby caiman must break the shell, with the egg-tooth on its snout, in order to emerge, the egg-tooth then being shed. Just before hatching, the babies start to croak. The mother, who has remained near the nest, on hearing this, begins to scrape the top from the nest to help their escape. The young caimans are like the parents except for having relatively larger eyes and shorter snouts. In most species they are coloured like the adults; dark or olive brown on the back, lighter on the flanks and dull white on the belly, with various dark blotches and patches, but the black caiman is a glossy

black when adult, with the underside white or yellow, but the young are black with yellow bands.

Baby caimans are nearly 1 ft long but may grow rapidly to 2 ft at the end of the first year, and possibly reaching 5 ft at the age of 5 years.

Caimans hunt by taste

It is usually said that caimans, like crocodiles and alligators, find their prey by smell. This is not borne out by tests made on a variety of crocodilians kept in captivity. These tests suggest that sight and taste are the important senses in the search for food. First of all a crocodilian closes both its nostrils and its ears when submerged, so smell and hearing are out of action, at least when it is under water. Then, we know the eyes are adapted to night vision because they show a slit pupil by day and a wide-open rounded pupil at night, and presumably sight is used both underwater and on land. More refined details about sight have been given by Zdenek Vogel, the Czech zoologist, who found that caimans appear to be able to recognize colours, can distinguish the outlines of large objects up to 33 ft away, and can detect sharp movements made 100 ft or more away.

His tests on the way they detect their food were even more decisive. Dried blood put into a tank where they were swimming produced no reaction, nor did washed meat hung in the water on a string or placed on a rock. Even hungry caimans ignored these but swallowed food eagerly when it was placed in their mouths. They seemed not to be affected by paraffin poured into the water until they opened their mouths and got it on their tongues. Similarly, meat that tinged the water red produced no reaction until the water touched their tongues.

The conclusion seems to be, therefore, that the main sense-organs used in hunting are the taste-buds on the tongue, used when in the water, and sight, used when the caiman is above or out of water.

class	**Reptilia**
order	**Crocodilia**
family	**Alligatoridae**
genera & species	***Caiman crocodylus*** *spectacled* ***C. latirostris*** *broad snouted* ***Melanosuchus niger*** *black* ***Paleosuchus palpebrosus*** } *smooth* ***P. trigonatus*** } *fronted*

Okapia

Camel

There are two species of camel: the Arabian or one-humped and the Bactrian or two-humped. The first is not known as a wild animal, though the second survives in the wild in the Gobi desert. A dromedary is a special breed of the one-humped camel, used for riding, although the name is commonly but wrongly used to denote the Arabian camel as a whole.

Camels have long legs and a long neck, coarse hair and tufted tails. Their feet have two toes united by a tough web, with nails and tough padded soles. The length of head, neck and body is up to 10 ft, the tail is 1½ ft long, height at the shoulder is up to 6 ft, and the weight is up to 1100 lb.

Habits

The wild camels of the Gobi desert are active by day, associating in groups of half-a-dozen, made up of one male and the rest females. They are extremely shy and make off at first sight of an intruder, moving with a characteristic swaying stride, due to the fore and hind legs on each side moving together. Their shyness may be partly due to persecution in former times.

It is often said that a camel cannot swim. Reports suggest they do not readily take to water, but they have been seen swimming.

Adaptations to desert life

Everything about a camel, both its external features and its physiology, show it to be adapted to life in deserts. Its eyes have long lashes which protect them from wind-blown sand. The nostrils are muscular so they can be readily closed, or partly closed to keep out sand. The form of the body, with the long neck and long legs, provides a large surface area relative to the volume of the body, which allows for easy loss of heat.

The camel's physiology shows other adaptations which provide protection from overheating, and help it to withstand dessication and to indulge in physical exertion with a minimum of feeding and drinking. These characteristics are often seen in stories of journeys made across waterless deserts. Many of these are exaggerated, but even those that are true are remarkable enough. There is one instance of a march through Somalia of 8 days without water and in Northern Australia a journey of 537 miles was made, using camels which were without a drink for 34 days. Most of the camels in this second journey died, but a few that were able to graze dew-wetted vegetation survived.

Most desert journeys are made in winter, however, and during that season even a man can go without drinking if he feeds largely on juicy fruits and vegetables. Knut Schmidt-Nielsen tested camels in the desert winter and found that even on a completely dry diet, camels could go several weeks without drinking, although they lost water steadily through their skin and their breath as well as in the urine and faeces. Normally, however, a camel feeds on desert plants with a high water content.

Do camels store water?

There are many stories of travellers in the desert killing a camel and drinking the water contained in its stomach. From these arose the myth, which has not yet been completely killed, that a camel stores water in its stomach. Pliny (AD 23-79), the Roman naturalist, first set it on record. Buffon

One-humped camels drinking at a water-hole in the desert. Having taken their fill of water, camels can survive for several days in the desert without drinking, or for several weeks if they have access to succulent desert plants. Water is drawn from the body tissues to maintain the fluid in the blood.

(1707-1788) and Cuvier (1769-1832), celebrated French scientists, accepted it. Owen (1804-1892) and Lyddeker (1849-1915), British anatomists and zoologists, supported it.

In 1801 George Shaw, British zoologist, wrote of a camel having four stomachs with a fifth bag which serves as a reservoir for water. Everard Home, the Scottish surgeon, dissected a camel and in 1806 published his celebrated drawing of alleged water pockets in the first two compartments of the stomach, a drawing which has many times been reproduced in books, and which has served to bolster the story. It was not until the researches of Schmidt-Nielsen and his team, working in the Sahara in 1953-4, that the full story emerged. In the living camel, these pockets are filled with an evil-smelling soup, the liquefied masticated food, which might be drunk, so saving his life, by a man crazy for water—but not otherwise.

Another of the camel's achievements which served to support the story is its ability to drink 27 gallons of water, or more, in 10 minutes. It will do so only to replenish the body supply after intense dessication. In those 10 minutes a camel will pass from an emaciated animal, showing its ribs, to a normal condition. This is something few other animals can do. But the water does not stay in the stomach; it passes into the tissues, and a camel after a long drink looks swollen.

A camel can lose water equal to 25% of its body weight and show no signs of distress. A man losing 12% of his body water is in dire distress because this water is drawn from his tissues and his blood. The blood becomes thick and sticky, so that the heart has greater difficulty in pumping. A camel loses water from its tissues but not from the blood, so there is no strain on the heart, and an emaciated camel is capable of the same physical exertion as normal. The

mechanism for this is not known. The only obvious difference between the blood of a camel and any other mammal is that its red corpuscles are oval instead of being discoid.

The camel's hump

The hump contains a store of fat and it has often been argued that this can be converted to water, and therefore the hump is a water reserve. The hump of the Arabian camel may contain as much as 100 lb of fat, each pound of which can yield 1·1 lb of water, or over 13 gallons for a 100 lb hump. To convert this, however, extra oxygen is needed, and it has been calculated that the breathing needed to get this extra oxygen would itself lead to the loss of more than 13 gallons of water as vapour in the breath. The fat stored in the hump is broken down to supply energy, releasing water which is lost. The hump is thus really a reserve of energy.

Other physiological advantages possessed by a camel are that in summer it excretes less urine and, more important, it sweats little. The highest daytime temperature is 40°C/105°F but during the night it drops to 34°C/93°F. A man's temperature remains constant at just under 39°C/100°F and as soon as the day starts to warm up he begins to feel the heat. A camel starts with a temperature of 34°C/93°F at dawn and does not heat up to 40°C/105°F until nearly midday. A camel's coat provides insulation against the heat of the day and it keeps the animal warm during the cold desert nights.

With all these advantages, camels should be even-tempered, but everyone agrees that they are bad-tempered to a degree. One writer has described them as stupid, unwilling, recalcitrant, obnoxious, untrustworthy and openly vicious, with an ability to bite destructively. There is a traditional joke that there are no wild camels, nor any

tame ones.

The power of the bite is linked with the camel's unusual dentition. At birth it has six incisors in both upper and lower jaws, a canine on each side, then a premolar followed by a gap before the cheek teeth are reached. As the young camel grows, it quickly loses all but the outside incisors of the six in the upper jaw and these take on a similar shape to the canines. So in making a slashing bite a camel has, in effect, double the fang capacity of a dog.

Breeding

A baby camel is a miniature of its parents, apart from its incisors, its soft fleece, lack of knee pads and hump. There is a single calf, exceptionally two, born 370—440 days after conception. Its only call is a soft *baa*. It can walk freely at the end of the first day but is not fully independent until 4 years old, and becomes sexually mature at 5 years. Maximum recorded life is 50 years.

Origins of the camel

Camels originated in North America, where many fossils have been found of camels, small and large, with short necks or long, as in the giraffe-like camels. The smallest was the size of a hare, the largest stood 15 ft at the shoulder. As the species multiplied there was one migration southwards into South America and another northwestwards, and then across the land-bridge where the Bering Straits now are, into Asia. As the numerous species died out, over the last 45 million years, the survivors remained as the S. American llamas and Asiatic camels.

A few species reached eastern Europe and died out. None reached Africa. Until 6 000 years or more ago there was only the one species in Asia, the two-humped Bactrian camel. The date is impossible to fix with

A Brown

1 In a sandstorm the long lashes protect the camel's eyes, and its nostrils can be closed.
2 Camels develop leathery callosities on their knees and other joints through kneeling down for loading.
3 The two-humped camel is more heavily built than the one-humped camel and is more suitable as a pack animal.

Zool. Soc. London

▽ The domesticated camel does many tasks once carried out by man. Here, while his keeper sleeps, the camel draws water from the well.

G Mundey

Geoffrey Kinns: AFA

DC Pike: Photo Res.

Okapia

△ Dromedaries are the
riding strain of the
one-humped camel,
and can travel 100
miles in a day.

Robert Burton

◁ Camels have been
used as pack animals
since early times, and
can carry a load of
about 400 lb.

487

◁ Camel herd of an Arabian caravan. A miniature from a manuscript of about the 12th century illustrates the work of the poet Harari. (Cairo)

▷ Camels belonging to the Bedouin tribesmen drinking at a water trough in Saudi Arabia.

Mansell

certainty, as is the date when the one-humped camel came into existence, but the evidence suggests that it is a domesticated form derived from the Bactrian camel. Both readily interbreed, and the offspring usually have two humps, the hind hump smaller than that in front.

Surprisingly, the first record of a one-humped camel is on pottery from the sixth dynasty of Ancient Egypt (about 3 500 BC) for the camel was not known in the Nile Valley until 3 000 years later. Its representation on the pottery may have been inspired by a wandering camel train from Asia Minor. Meanwhile, on Assyrian monuments dated 115–1102 BC, and from then onwards, the camel appears quite often, and when the Queen of Sheba visited King Solomon in Jerusalem, in 955 BC, she brought with her draught camels. The name seems to be from the Semitic *gamal* or *hamal*, meaning 'carrying a burden'.

The one-humped camel was presumably selectively bred from domesticated two-humped camels, in Central Asia, by peoples who left no records. It is also suggested that the nickname 'ship of the desert' is derived from 'animal brought in a ship from the desert' by mis-translation – a reference to the Assyrian habit of naming an animal according to the place from which it came. Presumably this would mean camels were brought by ship across the Persian Gulf.

Feral camels

Today the Bactrian camel is confined to Asia but most of the 3 million Arabian camels are on African soil. Some have, however, been introduced into countries far from Africa or Asia. In 1622 some were taken to Tuscany where a herd still lives on the sandy plains near Pisa. On the plains of Guadalquiver are feral camels taken to Spain by the Moors earlier still. Camels were taken to South America in the 16th century by the Spanish conquistadors but these have died out. Others were taken to Virginia in 1701, and there was a second importation into the United States in 1856. The survivors from these were still running wild in the deserts of Arizona and Nevada in 1915. Camels were taken to Northern Australia, and there also they have reverted to the wild.

For a long time text books reiterated that no camels are now known in the wild state. Yet they have been mentioned in the Chinese literature since the 5th century, and Marco Polo wrote about them. Then, in 1879, Nikolai Przewalski reported wild two-humped camels still living around Lake Lob, southeast of the Gobi desert. The local people told him they had been numerous a few decades prior to his visit but that they hunted them for their hides and flesh. There were reports also of camels in the

Gobi, but nobody was prepared to say whether these were truly wild or merely feral camels. In 1945, the Soviet zoologist AG Bannikov rediscovered them and in 1955 a Mongolian film unit secured several shots of them.

These Gobi camels are two-humped but the humps are small. They are swift, with long slender legs, small feet and no knee pads. Their coat is short, the ears smaller than in the domesticated camels, and the coat is a brownish-red.

The Mongolian film shows the Gobi camel to be different from the typical Bactrian and Arabian camels, and it would be not unreasonable to conclude that it represents the ancestral stock from which the other two were domesticated.

class	**Mammalia**	
order	**Artiodactyla**	
suborder	**Tylopoda**	
family	**Camelidae**	
genus & species	*Camelus dromedarius* 1-humped camel	
	Camelus bactrianus 2-humped camel	

Courtesy of the American Museum of Natural History

◁◁ Fossil camel skeleton reassembled from bones left about 20 million years ago in Nebraska, USA.

◁ Everard Home's drawing of alleged water pockets in the camel's stomach.

Canada goose

The Canada goose is a large grey-brown goose with black head and neck and a white patch extending from the chin, up the cheeks to behind the eyes. The tail is black while the feathers around the base of the tail are white. The bill and legs are black. The Canada goose is sometimes confused with the barnacle goose (see p. 289), but the latter is smaller, has a wholly white face, black breast and light underparts.

Range and habits

Canada geese live in Alaska, Canada, and the northern parts of the United States, migrating southwards as far as the Gulf of Mexico in winter. The species became known to Europeans when they began to settle in North America, around Newfoundland and Hudson's Bay. Live birds were brought back to Europe and domesticated in the 17th century, and in the 18th century they were described as being very familiar in England where they could be found breeding on lakes, in many country estates.

In habits, the Canada goose differs from the barnacle goose by preferring inland areas, frequenting grassland, lakes and marshlands, or even parkland, although it is also found on estuaries and seashores. It is gregarious outside the breeding season, forming groups of 200–300. In America it stays aloof from other species, but in Britain will sometimes mix with other geese.

Grazers on land and sea

The bulk of the food of the Canada goose is vegetable. It grazes on grasslands and on the rushes and sedges in marshes.

Around the sea shore, sea-lettuce, eel-grass and various algae are eaten. During their spring migration, Canada geese can be a considerable pest when flocks of them descend on fields of sprouting grain. Grazing the shoots does no permanent damage to the crop, but sometimes the seeds are pulled up. The swelling buds of trees and bushes are also eaten at this time. After the breeding season, when the geese are moving south, they graze in stubble fields.

Canada geese have favourite feeding grounds. They generally congregate in areas where food is abundant at that particular season, usually in the early morning, but where persecuted they take to feeding at night. The feeding flocks are guarded by sentries that warn the flock of approaching danger. The sentries are relieved at intervals so that they may take their turn in feeding.

During the breeding season, the geese turn to a more aquatic diet. They feed on the water plants and also take worms, insects, snails, crustaceans and perhaps small fish. When feeding in the water they dip their long necks into the water and up-end like ducks.

Mates are loyal for life

Canada geese mate for life and arrive at the breeding grounds already in pairs. Nevertheless, courtship and fighting take place on the breeding grounds where the ganders drive others from their chosen mates. In driving an adversary away, the gander advances with neck held out horizontally and bill open. At the same time he hisses and rustles his plumage. After vanquishing the opposition, the gander returns to his mate uttering the 'triumph note' and they both perform a 'celebration dance' with sinuous movements of their necks.

Nesting begins in March or April. The exact date depends on latitude, being later

▽ *Canada geese parents guard their young in the water. Males and females have similar adult plumage.*

▽ *In flight Canada geese are unmistakable with their black head and neck, and white cheeks and breast.*

J Van Wormer: Photo Res.

Russ Kinne: Photo Res.

in northern regions. It may be delayed by up to a fortnight in bad weather. The nests are normally built on the ground near water but, especially in areas liable to flooding, Canada geese may nest on rocky ledges or in trees. In Britain they sometimes take over the deserted nests of birds of prey. The nest is lined with grass, reeds and down. The normal number of eggs in a clutch is 5–6 but 2–11 have been recorded. They are brooded by the female alone. However, throughout the 28-day incubation period the gander stands guard. The guarding is more than a ritual; the ganders defend their offspring vigorously and there is a record of a man being knocked off his horse by a Canada goose that hit him so hard that it killed itself.

As soon as the chicks have hatched, the two parents lead them down to water, where they swim out, gander leading and goose bringing up the rear. When the nest is in a tree it is reported that the goose pushes the newly-hatched chicks over the side with her bill.

At a very early age the chicks can dive and they are fully grown at 6 weeks, weighing about 10 lb, and having the characteristic adult plumage.

Enemies

Before they can fly, young geese have many enemies, attacking them both from the air and from underwater. Canada geese, migrating up and down America, are shot as they feed in the fields or as they land on lakes, lured down by decoys or tame geese.

Arctic foxes prey on Canada geese, especially in years when their normal prey, small mammals, is scarce.

Harbinger of spring

The arrival of the Canada geese in the northern regions of America has always been the signal that spring has come. The month that they arrive is known to the Indians around Hudson's Bay as the Goose Moon. The early European settlers depended a great deal on the geese, killing several thousand a year and preserving them in barrels of salt for winter use. To shoot them, they used the same method as is used today. Hides made of boughs were set up at intervals across the marshes and men would lie in wait for the geese to land. Decoys were used to lure the geese, and the Indians would attract them by mimicking their honking.

The migrations of the Canada geese have been studied for many years. Their speed as they fly in V-shaped or W-shaped formations has been recorded as 60 mph by following them in aeroplanes. However, the overall movement up the continent is much slower, taking as much as 2 months, for the geese move slowly north as the temperature of the air rises.

The geese that wintered the farthest south are the first to move. They gather in restless flocks, honking to each other and preening their feathers in preparation for the long flight. At first they move only 9 miles a day, but this is increased to 30 later as the impetus of the movement increases. This is also related to the warming of the atmosphere, for it has been shown that the advancing geese keep level with the 2°C temperature line as it moves north.

class	**Aves**
order	**Anseriformes**
family	**Anatidae**
genus & species	***Branta canadensis***

WM Scott

The Canada goose is the most widespread, and the best known goose in North America. It was introduced into England over 200 years ago.

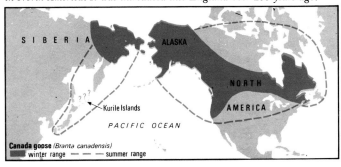

Canada goose *(Branta canadensis)*
■ winter range – – – summer range

Canary

The canary is a finch of the subfamily Carduelinae, $5\frac{1}{2}$ in. long and weighing $\frac{1}{2}$ oz., olive streaked with brown and black and greenish yellow on the breast. The wild form lives on the Canary Islands, the Azores and Madeira. It was imported into Europe probably in the 16th century, and selective breeding has produced a number of colour varieties, the most common ones being pale yellow, bright yellow, yellow tinged with orange, mottled or streaked with brown or black. Some varieties have a crested head. Mules, or hybrids, are readily produced by crossing with the greenfinch, linnet, siskin, citril finch and bullfinch. Popular and hardy breeds are the border, Yorkshire and Norwich, the last two being more than $5\frac{1}{2}$ in. long. The roller canary is kept purely for its song. Weight of domestic varieties varies from $\frac{1}{2}-1$ oz.

Sociable songsters

Canaries live in bushes and clumps of trees, readily coming into gardens, orchards and vineyards. They are sociable birds, with similar habits to other finches, and the main interest, in view of their popularity as caged songbirds, is in their song. This is a typical finch song and, as in other birds, is used basically for announcing to other birds of the species that a male is in occupation of a territory. The song of the wild canary is like that of the ordinary caged canary with a few harsher phrases interspersed.

Although domesticated canaries will mimic to some extent the songs of other birds, or imitate human speech, most of their song is built-in, almost complete from birth. A young canary hand-reared in isolation and allowed to hear only the song of the nightingale will use a song intermediate between a canary and a nightingale. If later placed with other canaries it will tend to lose the nightingale part of its song. Consequently, canaries selectively bred for colour and form have a song very near that of their wild brethren. The roller, on the other hand, with its 'improved' song has gained this by selection, not by imitation. Its song differs from those of the wild and the border canaries in quality, pitch and time-pattern.

Bird-fanciers use schoolmaster-canaries for training other birds. It is unlikely that these educate the others; they probably stimulate competition, as if they were competing for territory, so bringing out the best in their pupils.

Feeding

The main food is small seeds of low-growing herbaceous plants but canaries also take leaf and fruit buds.

Blind and naked babies

The wild canary builds high up in thick shrubs or trees. The hen chooses the nesting site and does most of the building, the cock helping little. The saucer-shaped nest is made of grass, roots and moss, lined with

John Markham

△ *The wild canary is mainly green in colour.*
▽ *Domestic canary variety with a crested head.*

▽ *Selective breeding of the wild canary has also produced the familiar yellow variety.*

Okapia

492

hair and feathers. Building activity reaches its peak 4 days before the first egg is laid and the 1–6, usually 3, pale blue eggs are laid at 24-hour intervals. The eggs hatch in 14 days, the babies being at first blind and naked except for a small amount of down. The abdomen is distended but grows smaller as the yolksac is absorbed. The eyes open about 7 days after hatching. Feathers then begin growing, and the plumage is complete within a month. The young leave the nest in 3 weeks and become independent 36 days after hatching.

History of domestication

The precise date of the introduction of the canary into Europe is not known. The place is believed to have been on the mainland of Italy opposite the island of Elba. There, canaries were released and would probably have become naturalised had they not been captured in such numbers that they were eradicated. The date of introduction can only be guessed from the fact that Gesner, the Swiss naturalist, writing in 1585, mentions the canary as a cage-bird and Aldrovandus, the Italian naturalist, writing in 1610, gives a full description of it. Belon, the French naturalist, made no mention of the bird in his book published in 1555. So somewhere between 1555 and 1585 the canary was becoming known in Europe.

The first use of the term 'canary-bird' in England was in 1576, and oddly enough the first reference to Canary, the island, was later, in 1592. The fashion for keeping canaries must have spread rapidly, so that canaries in cages became a common sight, because by 1673 'canary-bird' meant a jail-bird in criminal slang.

There are a few other 'straws in the wind' that help us to piece together the early history of the canary in Europe. George Gascoigne, the English poet, who died in 1577, tells us in his *Complaint of Phylomena*: 'Canara byrds come in to beare the bell', and Francis Willoughby, noted English naturalist, who died in 1672, recorded in his *History of Birds*, published in 1676, that canaries were common in England.

Laurence Aldersey, merchant in the City of London, described in 1581 his visit to Augusta, in Germany, being taken to the 'State House, which is very faire, and beautifull. Then he brought me to the finest garden, and orchard, that ever I sawe in my life; for there was in it a place for canairie birdes, as large as a faire chamber, trimmed with wier both above and beneath, with fine little branches of trees for them to sit in, which was full of those canarie birdes.'

This seems to pinpoint Germany as a centre for the early breeding of canaries, reflected perhaps in the Hartz Mountain breed and in the early work done in neighbouring Austria on training canaries to mimic the nightingale, which led to the roller canary.

The group of islands we now call the Canaries were known in Roman times as the *Fortunatae Insulae* (Happy Islands), and one of them was called *Canaria* (from the Latin *canis*) because of the large dogs kept on it. Later this name was used for the whole

The canary has been popular as a cage bird in Europe from the 16th century because of its beautiful song. It sings especially well when outside in the sunshine.

group of islands, which were conquered by Spain at the end of the 15th century. It was doubtless this final conquest, after nearly a century of unsuccessful military expeditions, that led to the canary bird finding its way to Europe. If we link Aldersey's account of the well-stocked aviary in Germany with an extract from the writings of another author, it seems reasonable to suppose that, once the export of canaries had been started, it soon became 'big business'. This extract is from *His Pilgrimes*, by the Rev S Purchas, in the 4th volume, edition 1669. Writing of the neighbouring Azores, where canaries were also native, Purchas noted that one of the islands had canary birds 'which are there by thousands, where many birders take them, and thereof make a daily living, by carrying them into divers places.'

There is sufficient here to suggest that the

history of the canary is closely paralleled, in more modern times, by that of the budgerigar (see p. 430) of which we can be more certain. There is the first exporting of the bird, a growing popularity, selective breeding, resulting in a very short time in a number of colour varieties, the fashion spreading and leading to 'big business', until finally the species becomes better known in its domesticated form than in the wild, and differs markedly from the wild form.

class	**Aves**
order	**Passeriformes**
family	**Fringillidae**
genus & species	*Serinus canarius*

493

Cape buffalo

The Cape buffalo has the reputation of being the most dangerous of the African big-game animals. This bulky ox-like creature stands 4–5 ft at the shoulder and adult bulls weigh nearly a ton. The head and shoulders are heavily built and support the characteristic large horns that spring from broad bases, sometimes meeting at the midline of the forehead, and curving first down, then up, to finish in a point. In some cases the horns point back rather than up. The record span for the horns is 56 in. The coat is brownish-black, thick in young buffaloes and sparse in older individuals. Old animals are sometimes naked in places.

At one time it was thought that another species, the bush-cow or forest buffalo, lived in the equatorial forests from Senegal to eastern Congo. It was smaller, reddish-brown in colour and its much smaller horns pointed straight back rather than up. Although, by all appearances, distinct from the Cape buffalo, it is now recognized that the forest buffalo is merely a different form. At one time 15 species of African buffalo were recognized. Later, Lyddeker, one of the greatest authorities on African animals, recognized only one species but divided it into 21 local races. Nowadays, on the basis of careful study of anatomy and behaviour, the forest buffalo is considered to be no more than a form adapted by its small size and back-pointing horns, to living in thick forests.

Dangerous only if panicked

The Cape, or African, buffalo was once common throughout Africa south of the Sahara, but its range is now restricted. Hunting has taken its toll, and towards the end of the last century, Cape buffaloes contracted a disease called rinderpest from domestic cattle. This decimated the population over the greater part of South and East Africa, and in places only isolated populations, where the disease did not reach, have survived.

Cape buffaloes are gregarious, living in herds ranging from a few dozen to several hundreds, led by an old female. Although numbers are much reduced herds 1–2 thousand strong may still be seen in some places, such as the Kruger National Park.

Like many animals in tropical or subtropical regions, Cape buffaloes are most active in the early morning and evening. During the heat of the day they lie up in the shade, and at night they rest and chew the cud. They are never found far from water and go down to drink during the morning and evening. After drinking they enjoy splashing about and wallowing in the mud.

Under normal circumstances, Cape buffalo are not aggressive; the danger lies in their panicking. If they are approached cautiously across open country, so that they can see what is coming, the only reaction will be some of the bulls coming out to investigate, lifting their muzzles and flaring

△ *With its large horns and heavy build, the Cape buffalo is probably the most formidable and dangerous big-game animal in Africa.*

△ *Cape buffalo bull making overtures to a cow which looks on with apparent indifference.*
▽ *Stampeding buffalo charge at speeds up to 35 mph. Even heavy bore rifle shots may not stop them.*

their nostrils in a characteristic fashion. If they are approached unexpectedly from behind, however, the herd is likely to retreat back along its tracks in a panic. The only thing to do in these circumstances is to run behind a tree or ant-hill.

Feeding
The Cape buffalo is a grazer, its muzzles being flattened to square off with the ground. It will also browse on leaves and twigs when grass is rather sparse.

Breeding
The time of mating varies within the range, in some places occurring nearly all the year round. The older bulls are often driven out of the herd by the somewhat younger and more powerful bulls.

The single calves are born after a gestation of around 340 days. Within 10 minutes the calf is able to stand up.

Lion is the only enemy
Lions are the natural enemies of these powerful animals, although the buffaloes often kill their attackers. In Zambia, Cape buffalo are often the main prey of lions. It is usually the young and weak animals that are killed. It has been said that the lions can cause herds to panic, perhaps driving them into an ambush where other lions are lying in wait.

As bad as it looks
It is a debatable, but academic, point as to whether the Cape buffalo is the most dangerous animal to man in Africa, or only the second or third. There are several features of their behaviour, however, that make them very fear-inspiring. We have seen how a herd, perhaps several hundred in number and nearly as many tons in weight, will charge in a blind panic, surely a more terrifying sight than a single hissing snake or roaring lion. To the onlooker the results are worse, for even a single buffalo will produce the same result as a herd of buffalo, by its habit of trampling and goring its victim until little that is recognisable remains. Or a herd may pass the body of their enemy from one pair of horns to another, round and round, until it is dead.

Another unpleasant feature for someone on the receiving end of a buffalo's charge is

Cape buffalo graze in large herds over grassy parts of Africa south of the Sahara. Cattle egrets feed on ground-living insects disturbed by the buffalo as they feed.

that even a heavy bore rifle may not stop it; the buffalo charges with the head up, so that the heavy bases of the horns protect the brain, and the thick, muscular neck slows down any bullet entering the body.

If the buffalo is wounded, the danger is increased for it now becomes vindictive, and seems to go to great lengths to wreak revenge. Once wounded, it will often double back in a semicircle on its tracks and hide up in a bush or some other shelter. It is not deliberately waiting in ambush, but is now so inflamed that the mere sight of its pursuer coming past trailing it, is sufficient to make it charge out.

The tables may now be turned, with the hunter finding himself up a tree with the irate buffalo underneath. There have been reports, albeit unconfirmed, of hunters being caught in low trees and dying slowly and

painfully from having all their exposed skin licked off by the buffaloes' rasp-like tongues.

One anecdote about an enraged Cape buffalo is amusing rather than horrifying, at least at second-hand. One day a District Commissioner was called out to shoot a buffalo that was in a furious temper, charging down native huts and chasing the occupants. The reason for its ire was easy to see. It was hobbling about on three legs with the fourth caught on one of its horns. Presumably it had slipped while scratching itself.

class	**Mammalia**
order	**Artiodactyla**
family	**Bovidae**
genus & species	*Syncerus caffer*

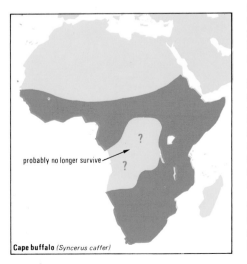

probably no longer survive →

Cape buffalo *(Syncerus caffer)*

Okapia

Hunting dogs work in a pack, chasing, tiring and overtaking their prey, such as this wildebeeste, and then tear at the throat and flanks with their slashing canine teeth.

Cape hunting dog

This is a ferocious carnivore only distantly related to the domestic dog. Unlike true dogs, foxes, wolves and jackals the Cape hunting dog, or African wild dog, has only four toes on the front foot, that is, the dew claws are missing. It stands just over 2 ft at the shoulder and measures 4 ft from nose to bushy tail. The large, round ears and mottled black, yellow and white coat give the dog a bizarre patchwork look. It has an unpleasant odour, and a weird call that has been described as being like an oboe or the whinny of a horse.

Hunters with a base camp

The range of the hunting dogs extends from south of the Sahara desert to South Africa, wherever there is open savannah country. They live in packs of 4—60, usually around a dozen. The packs are nomadic, staying in one area as long as there is an abundant supply of food, then moving on. When the pack arrives in an area, it sets up a base camp, not far from water, from which hunting parties set out. The camp is often in the abandoned burrows of other animals, or by a water hole. Here the pups are left with guardians while the rest of the pack ranges across the countryside. If food is plentiful the pack will not range far, but as it becomes scarce they hunt over a large area, perhaps as much as 80 square miles.

Time Life Inc.

Killer packs

Hunting dogs hunt systematically as a pack, running down their prey and eating it even before it is dead. They will kill more than they need, merely, it seems, for the sake of killing. One pack that was observed for a long period in the Serengeti Plains had two regular hunting times: 6.30−7.30 (sunrise) and 18.00−19.00 (sunset).

When the dogs are at rest, their prey— mainly antelopes, although small mammals, such as cane rats, and birds will be eaten in times of shortage—take little notice of them. They will wander, grazing, to within 100 yd or so of the hunting dogs, but as soon as the dogs begin to move, the antelopes and other big mammals take flight. Gazelles, such as Thomson's and Grant's gazelles, take flight when they see a hunting pack half a mile away, although the dogs can easily run them down despite this start.

Unlike the cat family, who are sprinters, giving up if the quarry is not caught after the initial burst of speed, dogs are long distance runners. Their speed is not impressive, but they are persevering, have great staying power and run down their prey after a long chase. Anyone who has trained for sport will appreciate these tactics; it is always easier to cover a lot of ground by jogging than by sprinting and slowing. Frequently the prey will jink to avoid its immediate pursuer and this will bring it closer to one of the others who will be in a position to slash at it with its canine teeth.

The quarry is worn down more quickly by the dogs snapping chunks of flesh out of its flanks, so it soon becomes weak from loss of blood, and the pack descends on it and eats it alive. First to be eaten are the entrails, which are rich in vitamins and other essentials, but eventually there is little left except the skull.

Wildebeeste do not run from the hunting dog packs. The bulls move forward and try to repel the dogs by charging them, but the dogs avoid these attacks and dodge round the bulls to where the calves and cows are huddled. Providing these stay in a tight bunch they are safe from the hunters, but as soon as a calf becomes separated it is seized. Not only do such large animals as wildebeeste fall prey to hunting dogs, even lions have been attacked and killed.

497

Organised social life

The close-knit nature of the hunting dog pack is shown by their breeding behaviour. Pups are born at any time of the year after 7–11 weeks gestation, but there is some doubt as to the exact time. The pups are reared in a communal burrow, an abandoned aardvark hole for instance, and, what is most unusual, the adults share in rearing the pups. One of the few causes of disagreements among the pack members occurs when females compete for the care of a pup, for all the females nurse all the pups, and they will try to steal pups away from other females.

When the pack goes hunting, some

Man the only feared enemy

While in a pack, the hunting dogs need fear nothing except man, but lions have been seen investigating nursery burrows, which results in the pups being moved away.

Utopian society

We have seen how Cape hunting dogs cooperate in hunting and rearing their young, and it is tempting to compare the social life of these dogs with our own. It might be possible that the hunting dogs are leading the same sort of life as our ancestors did when they lived as hunters in small family units. It may have been the organisation of

individuals to come near each other without aggression. In our society these patterns can be summed up as good manners, but in other species there are also special patterns that allow individuals to live amicably.

To make life easy in the hunting dog pack, the dogs greet each other by pretending to beg food from each other, in the same way as the pups, by pushing at the other's mouth with the nose. By using this juvenile pattern of behaviour the dog that is being greeted does not become aggressive. Other juvenile behaviour is also used by the adults such as the males licking the females' udders or the female creeping under the male like a pup under its mother.

Immature Cape hunting dogs at play. Pups are born at any time of the year after 7—11 weeks gestation, being reared in a communal burrow.

females and certain males stay behind to guard the pups. When the hunters return, they disgorge some of their food to the pups and the guards. When the pups are very small, the females beg for extra meat from the hunting party and chew it up to give to the pups at intervals. The pups begin taking meat when a fortnight old, even though they are not weaned until 10–12 weeks. Like other young carnivores, the pups spend much time· in play simulating their hunting behaviour.

Because of the dogs' communal breeding habits it has been difficult to decide how many pups there are in a litter. From observations at zoos it seems that there may be as many as 19, although 6–8 would be nearer the normal.

baby-sitters while the main party went out hunting that allowed our pre-human ancestors to break from the baboon-like scavenging way of life, and become hunters. It would have been possible to take the children out to collect berries or birds' eggs, but they would have hampered a hunting expedition. A division of labour like this, with individuals carrying out different duties, is the hallmark of a society whether it be of men, hunting dogs or honeybees.

Most animals, including ourselves, do not like being crowded together. If one gets too close to another it is likely to be attacked or threatened. This is obviously a disadvantage for a social animal, as any commuter will realise, so in animal societies there are special patterns of behaviour which allow

In one way the hunting dog society, for all its ferocity in the hunt, is one stage nearer to perfection than ours. All hunting dogs are equal. There is no rank, as is found amongst wolves, each adult is qualified to perform every job whether it be hunting, feeding the pups or guarding them, and at the kill every dog gets its fair share.

class	**Mammalia**
order	**Carnivora**
family	**Canidae**
genus & species	*Lycaon pictus*

Capercaillie

Also spelt capercailzie (a name derived from the Gaelic for bird or old man of the wood) this is a large awe-inspiring game-bird, the males being nearly 3 ft long and the females 2 ft. Although it is like other game-birds in form, no other British game-bird approaches the capercaillie in size. The general colour of the male's plumage is a dark slaty grey with flecks of white on the body. The throat and sides of the head are black and the breast is glossy green-black. There is some bright red skin over the eye, the bill is whitish, and there is a 'beard' of greenish-black feathers like an inverted crest. The female is browner and can be confused with grouse, but it is larger than a grouse and has a red patch on the breast.

Capercaillies sometimes interbreed with black grouse, but usually the two species live in different localities and so do not mix.

Range dependent on forests

The range of capercaillies has diminished since coniferous forests have been cut down, though in places they have spread into new plantations. Their present range includes Scandinavia and eastern Europe across to Lake Baikal, roughly between latitudes 66 and 52 degrees North. These lines correspond approximately to the July temperature lines of 12°C/53°F in the north and 21°C/70°F in the south. Capercaillies are also found in much of Central Europe and the Balkans, Austria, Switzerland, southern Germany and eastern France. There are isolated populations in the Pyrenees and eastern Scotland. In eastern Siberia there is a second species of capercaillie.

The original populations in Ireland and Scotland were exterminated in the 18th century when the forests were destroyed. Then in 1837 and 1838 some capercaillies were imported from Sweden and released at Taymouth. They spread rapidly and are now found from Stirling to southeast Sutherland. Their numbers decreased in both World Wars because of extensive tree felling but now they are spreading into young conifer plantations.

The flight of the capercaillie is that of a typical game-bird: rapid wingbeats followed by a glide with down-curved wings. When flushed, they usually fly a short way only before landing. The takeoff is very noisy but as the flight levels off, it becomes rapid and silent, in the same manner as a wood-pigeon.

In the summer they are generally seen singly, but in winter they become gregarious, the males, especially, forming large parties.

Scots pine is winter food

The capercaillie lives almost entirely on plant food. A few beetles and other insects, mainly grubs, are taken, but most of these are probably eaten by accident along with plant material.

During the summer, a wide variety of plants is eaten, such as grass, heather flowers, berries and fruits of rowan, bramble,

Popperfoto

△ *The largest member of the grouse family, the male capercaillie has a wingspan of over 4 ft.*

▽ *The female's plumage is not as distinctive as the male's and she can be confused with a grouse.*

Popperfoto

499

Eric Hosking

Forestry Commission

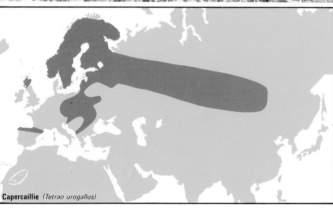

Capercaillie *(Tetrao urogallus)*

△ *The hen capercaillie, after mating, builds the nest and raises a family on her own. The nest is usually a hollow scraped in the undergrowth in forests or in heather in open country.*

△ *The capercaillie's food, especially in winter, includes the shoots, buds, needles, seeds, and young cones of the Scots pine. Little damage is done to mature pinewoods, but in newly-established plantations damage can be serious. All too often the bird pecks the leading bud out (as seen in this photograph) causing loss of growth and perhaps a distorted stem, which results from a new leader developing from a lower bud.*

▷ *During April and May the cock performs his courtship display. The head is held high up, the neck feathers are puffed out and the tail broadly fanned and held upright. At the same time a variety of calls are made.*

cranberry and hawthorn and seeds of violet and buttercup. In the autumn, about mid-November, both diet and habitat change as the capercaillies move from forests with little or no pine to those with pine predominating. At the same time they cease feeding on the ground and are mostly found in the trees. Their diet now consists mainly of the needles of Scots pine, together with twigs, buds and unopened cones. Other trees such as larch, spruce, occasionally some deciduous trees, and herbaceous plants, make up the rest of the capercaillies' winter food. Because they feed in trees they are little affected by snowfall.

Breeding

In April and May, usually starting at daybreak, the cock capercaillies gather in a tree, on a rock or on the ground, to display. Like other members of the grouse family, they perform an elaborate ceremonial, each bird defending a small territory. The neck is stretched up with the bill pointed to the sky so that the 'beard' is well displayed, and the tail is fanned and held vertically like a peacock's tail. While in this position the birds strut about rustling their wings and occasionally leaping as much as 3 ft into the air. At the same time they make various calls. One has been described as sounding like cats fighting in the distance or a man vomiting. Others are made up of noises such as steel on a whetstone and corks being drawn from bottles. These strange sounds can still be called a song as they have

the same function of establishing territory and attracting a mate as the songs of the familiar garden birds.

The hens attracted to these displays, mate with one of the cocks, then depart to raise families on their own. The nest, usually a hollow scraped in the ground, is made in the undergrowth in forests or in heather in open country. In the second half of April, 5–8, rarely 2–15, eggs are laid. Until the clutch is completed, the eggs are covered with vegetation such as pine needles, after which incubation begins, continuing for 29 days. As incubation begins when the clutch is complete, all the eggs develop together and hatch within 24 hours of each other. The chicks leave the nest when very young and are tended by the hen for some time. She protects them, luring away predators, such as foxes, by feigning injury. By limping away from the brood with one wing trailing as if broken, she attracts the attention of the predator who chases what appears to be an easy prey. Once the brood is safe, she flies up, leaving the predator baffled.

Cock capercaillies terrorize the forest

On several occasions cock capercaillies in the Scottish Highlands have been reported as terrorizing anyone who came near them. One which lived in a small wood in Angus was active each spring for 4 years. Humans were attacked vigorously with beak and

wings, and one ornithologist was driven backwards through the wood, defending himself with his camera tripod. Sheep wandering into the wood were driven away and a horse in a nearby field was so frightened that it stayed as far as possible from the wood. Another capercaillie made similar attacks on children as they went to school, but did not go so far as the first in attacking motor cars and vans.

Such aggressive individuals must be rare, for the general rule is for an animal to flee in the face of possible predators. This aggressive behaviour has not been recorded from other parts of the capercaillie's range, for on the continent there are more natural enemies such as wolverines and Arctic foxes to despatch a capercaillie that thought valour the better part of discretion. Also the hunting of capercaillies is more intense on the continent and an aggressive capercaillie is a sitting target.

class	**Aves**
order	**Galliformes**
family	**Tetraonidae**
genus & species	***Tetrao urogallus*** *European capercaillie*
	T. parvirostris *Siberian capercaillie*

Capuchin

A very entertaining monkey, the capuchin is the one most used by organ grinders, and is now the commonest monkey in captivity in Europe and the United States. Authorities disagree as to the number of species of capuchin. The latest information is that there are four species divisible into 33 subspecies. The four species fall into two natural groupings, tufted and untufted. The first group, with one species, is the white-throated capuchin. It has tufts of hair over the eyes or along the side of the head and has a uniform coat of greyish-brown hair. The other has no tufts on the head and has a patterned coat with patches of white on the face, throat and chest. They are small monkeys, head and body measuring 12–15 in. The tail, which may be 2 ft long, is prehensile and is used to pick up objects out of reach of the hands.

The name capuchin is derived from the resemblance of the hair on the head to the pointed cowl or capuche of Franciscan monks. The capuchins are also known as ring-tails from their habit of carrying the tail with the tip coiled up.

The home of the capuchins is in the forests of South America, especially those with no undergrowth. They range from Costa Rica to Paraguay and are also found on Trinidad and are generally confined to fairly low ground.

Gregarious life

Capuchins are strictly tree-dwellers; the weeping capuchins apparently leave the trees only to drink. They live in troops ranging from a small family party to a loose group of up to 40. Each troop keeps to regular tracks through the forest and has a small but regular range, which may overlap the ranges of other troops. Sometimes several troops may share a track, each using it at different times. The troop moves through the trees in single file and in a regular order. First come the half-grown young of both sexes, followed by the adult females and the adult males, the females with young bringing up the rear.

The main reason for the capuchins' popularity in zoo and laboratory is their intelligence, which is often as great as that of chimpanzees. Many tests have shown how they can use insight to work out problems, rather than use laborious trial-and-error attempts at solution. They will use sticks to draw food towards the bars of their cages, and get fruit suspended out of reach by moving a box under it and climbing up. They also work out their own problems spontaneously. One capuchin had the habit of throwing things at people. It realised that throwing missiles at their feet had little effect so it took to standing on a chair to get a higher trajectory. The same monkey learnt to use a hammer properly, and another, when too old to crack Brazil nuts in its teeth, smashed them with a marrow bone.

Okapia

The capuchin's name is derived from the resemblance of its hair on the head to the capuche of Franciscan monks. Capuchins live in troops which move over a small range in South American forests.

Diet of fruit and insects

Fruit is the main food of capuchins, and they will raid orange, maize and chocolate bean plantations. They eat no leaves or shoots but take any small animals they can find. Insects, especially butterflies, are caught on wing and small birds and mammals overpowered. Spiders and grubs are collected by prising up bark. Hard fruit, nuts, beetles and birds' eggs are banged against branches until soft or split open before being eaten.

Babies travel pick-a-back

Capuchins have one baby at a time, born after about 6 months gestation. For the first weeks of its life the baby lives on its mother's back, hanging on to her fur with its hands and feet and wrapping its tail around her body. It leaves this position only at feeding times. After a while the baby starts to crawl around its mother's back and examine things. It then begins to move away from her for short distances, while she holds it by the tail in case it slips and falls. A few months later the baby becomes much more independent and its mother will push it away if it tries to climb on her. This is not surprising, for capuchins grow very rapidly, and at 6 months are nearly full grown. During this time, the father also helps care for the baby, and if it becomes separated from its parents and cries, other members of the troop will come to its assistance and bring it back to the troop.

Few enemies

Capuchins are preyed on by jaguars and large birds of prey, but they are hunted little by man because their flesh is not so good to eat as that of the spider monkeys and woolly monkeys.

B Rensch

Monkey masterpieces

Whether we feel that having exhibitions of paintings by monkeys and apes, or paying for the privilege of owning them, is a waste of money or even a sign of imbecility, there is, nevertheless, good reason to study the scrawls and daubs that they produce. For one thing, the animals will paint of their own free will, once they have been shown how to use the materials. They must, therefore, get some satisfaction out of the activity, and it is worth examining the pictures to see whether the satisfaction is merely that of doing something active, or whether the animals are controlling the movement of pencil or brush, perhaps to produce something that is pleasing to them.

It seems that some of the paintings produced by capuchins, chimpanzees and gorillas are pleasing to the human eye otherwise they would not be bought and displayed. Analysis of them shows that there are certain basic patterns in monkey and ape painting. The simplest pictures are of scribbles, like those made by a child 12−18 months old. Also fan-shaped patterns of lines are produced. These can be pleasing to human eyes, but their production may be due to no more than the rhythmic movements of the arm. However, it is this rhythm that is pleasing, as is the balance, to left and right, of the paintings. Again this may be due merely to the properties of the optical system of the brain of the monkeys, leading them to make a balanced series of lines. But these properties of the brain probably serve also as the basis for the human pleasure in any balanced form. So here we may have the beginnings of an aesthetic sense apparently based on physical properties of nervous system and limbs. It is this that makes the study of monkey and ape painting worthwhile, to give us further insight into our own psychology.

△ *Pablo producing a simple picture of scribbles, like that of a child 12−18 months.*

▽ *The weeping capuchin, unlike other capuchins, will occasionally leave the trees to take a drink.*

Rudi Herzog

class	**Mammalia**
order	**Primates**
family	**Cebidae**
genus	***Cebus***

Capuchin monkey *(genus Cebus)*

503

Okapia

△ *The heavily-built capybara is the largest living rodent up to 4 ft long and weighing over 100 lb. It is inoffensive and can be tamed but does not thrive in captivity.*

Capybara

The capybara is the world's largest rodent. Also called water pig or water cavy, it looks like a huge guinea pig, but with a shorter body. The body is massive, the head proportionately large and the legs fairly short. Its coat of long coarse hair is sparse and coloured grey to reddish-brown, yellowish-brown on the underparts with some areas of black on the face, the outer surfaces of the limbs and the rump. The broad and deep head has small rounded ears, small eyes and nostrils all set high up. Each front foot has four toes with hoof-like claws, and there are three similar toes on each hind foot. All feet are slightly webbed. The overall length, including the very short tail, is up to 4 ft, the height at the shoulder 21 in. and the weight 120 lb. The male has a large gland of unknown function just in front of the eyes. The capybara ranges over northern South America, east of the Andes.

There is a second species in Panama, smaller and weighing up to 60 lb.

Runs like a horse

When alarmed, capybaras run like horses and will take refuge in water, swimming and diving with ease. They live in groups of up to 20 among dense vegetation in marshes and swamps, or in wooded areas around rivers and lakes. Normally they swim with little more than ears, eyes and nostrils showing above the water. When hard-pressed they can swim considerable distances underwater, coming up among water plants and exposing only the nostrils. Their voice consists of clicking sounds, high-pitched whistles and low grunts.

Vegetarian feeders

Wholly vegetarian, they feed on aquatic plants, often standing belly deep in water to do so. They also feed on grass and will some-

BH Reed

△ *Resting capybara. Each front foot has four slightly webbed toes with hoof-like claws.*

▽ *Young capybaras are well developed at birth but remain with the parents a long time.*

Okapia

504

△ *The capybara usually lives among dense vegetation in marshes and swamps, or in wooded areas around rivers and lakes. When alarmed it will run like a horse and makes for available water where it dives and swims with ease. It swims with little more than its ears, eyes, and nostrils showing.*

△ *The hair of the capybara is quite long and coarse to the touch. On the forehead just in front of the eyes is a large oil-secreting gland, but why it should be there is not known.*

Capybara *(Hydrochoerus hydrochaeris)*

△ *Capybaras live in swampy areas round the rivers of eastern S America. A smaller form* Hydrochoerus isphmius *lives in Panama.*

times graze with cattle. Occasionally they attack crops of cereals and fruits, such as melons, as a result of which they are hunted as pests. Normally they feed around dawn and dusk, but they may become wholly nocturnal where persecuted.

Well-developed babies
There is a single litter a year, of 2–8, after a gestation period of 119–126 days. The babies, born at an advanced stage of development as in their relative the guinea pig, weigh about 2½ lb. They remain with the mother until well on towards the next breeding season. The life span is up to 12 years.

The capybara, although well suited to life in zoological gardens, has not been frequently bred in captivity. The first report of a birth seems to be that of two young bred in the Zoological Gardens of London in 1874. San Diego Zoological Gardens have achieved the most successful breedings of this tropical species.

Completely defenceless
In addition to being hunted by man, capybaras are hunted by jaguars on land and fall prey to alligators and caimans in water. Inoffensive by nature, they are completely defenceless against a predator.

Neutral buoyancy
The capybara looks at first sight like a typical land animal. Anyone not acquainted with its habits would not suspect it was semi-aquatic, yet water is needed not only as a refuge, but for good health. If compelled to live long away from water a capybara suffers from a dry skin which soon becomes ulcerated; and it finds difficulty in mating and defaecating.

As we have seen, this large rodent is a good swimmer, yet it has few of the usual adaptations for this. Its toes are only partly webbed and its body is not streamlined, yet like the hippopotamus, of similar bulky

build, it is a graceful and accomplished swimmer. The secret lies in that, volume for volume, it is only slightly more heavy than water, due to its stored fat. With a bulky body containing plenty of fatty tissue to counterbalance the weight of the bony skeleton, as there is in the capybara, only a small force exerted by limbs is needed to give it the grace of a ballerina under water. Surprising as it may sound, that is an apt description of both the capybara and the hippopotamus when submerged. Their lumbering gait on land belies the poetry of their movements under water.

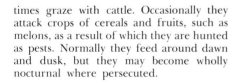

class	**Mammalia**
order	**Rodentia**
family	**Hydrochoeridae**
genus & species	*Hydrochoerus hydrochaeris*

Popperfoto

Eric Hosking

The caracal or desert lynx has a bad reputation as a killer but it can be readily tamed.
In India it was used to hunt for sport. A pair of caracals let loose at a flock of feeding
pigeons would strike several down in one second.

△ Aggressive snarl by the caracal. The long
lynx-like ear-tufts are used in signalling.
▷ Caracal leisurely stretched out with its prey.

Caracal

*Also known as desert lynx, the caracal is
regarded by some zoologists as akin to the
serval, one of the medium-sized cats, and
by others as a true lynx. In captivity it
has the cat-like habit of rubbing itself
against the bars of the cage and purring.
It is distinguished by its reddish-fawn,
short-haired coat, its large black ears with
very long ear-tufts, and its long, slender
legs. It has a 2 ft long head and body,
with a 10 in. tail, and stands up to 18 in.
at the shoulder. Its weight is up to 18 lb.
The range of the caracal covers savannah
and semi-desert throughout Africa and into
southwest Asia, including Arabia to
Afghanistan, and eastwards through Sind,
Punjab, and Kutch to the United Pro-
vinces of India. Throughout this extensive
range the animal is becoming scarce, and
in the Asian sector it is extremely rare.*

Playing skittles with pigeons
Caracals avoid forests and keep to sparse
bush and grassland, or to hilly country
with boulders. They can climb jackal-proof
fences to get among poultry, and are good
leapers. They are mainly nocturnal, so little
is known of their habits, but they will hunt
by day in cool or cloudy weather.

The caracal has a bad reputation as a
killer, but it can readily be tamed, and in
India was used to hunt for sport. A favourite
trick was to loose a pair of caracals at a
flock of pigeons feeding on the ground.
Each would strike down as many birds as
possible before the flock, rising in alarm,
could become fully airborne. One caracal
would strike down up to ten pigeons in a
second, which makes it credible that the
term lynx-eyed was derived from this
species. A caracal will strike birds down

that are already airborne, by rearing up on
its hindlegs or leaping anything up to 6 ft
into the air.

Small mammals and birds hunted
Caracals feed on a variety of animals up to
the size of young kudu and the smaller
antelopes, as well as rodents, such as jer-
boas, hares, monkeys, guinea fowl and fran-
colins, in addition to smaller birds. They
are said to leap onto a sitting ostrich and
kill it with a quick bite in the neck. They are
reported also to kill snakes.

Underground nurseries
The breeding season is September—December, and after a gestation of 9 weeks, a litter
of 2—4, sometimes 5, is born in an old
aardvark burrow, fox hole, or in a hollow
tree. Like any cat, the young are defended
against intruders, the parent showing de-
fiance by spitting in typical cat-fashion. The
kittens' first coat is bright reddish brown but
after a few months silvery hairs grow, making the colour more greyish red-brown.

Desert coats

We might say that the caracal has the
typical colour of desert, and it is a fact that,
with few exceptions, mammals living in
deserts and semi-deserts are coloured pale
buff to tawny or sandy red. The obvious
conclusion to draw is that these colours har-
monize with the colour of the earth and so
are a protective camouflage. Nevertheless,
other lynxes, living in the forests of northern Europe and America, are similarly
coloured. It is true that some, like the
Spanish lynx, may be spotted, but most of
them lack spots.

So far as the caracal is concerned, the
colour of its coat should have little value
for concealment since it is nocturnal. It is,
moreover, not only the ground animals
living in deserts that sport the sandy coats.

The eight species of bats living over the
Sahara, which spend the day in caves or
deep in clefts in the rocks, all have fur the
colour of the sand over which they fly.
Is it, then, the temperature, humidity or
some other factor that is responsible for
the colouring? The question has yet to be
answered. It is, however, worth recalling
what happens in the African pipistrelle bat
that ranges into southern Europe.

In Europe it is dark brown. Over the Al-
gerian hills it is green. The pipistrelles living
over the Sahara are sandy. All belong to
the same species. This suggests that the
colour has some value but it may be linked
with the climatic conditions. In introducing
cattle to these areas it is found that light-
coloured Jersey cattle stand up to tropical
conditions better than breeds with a dark
coat.

class	**Mammalia**
order	**Carnivora**
family	**Felidae**
genus & species	*Felis caracal*

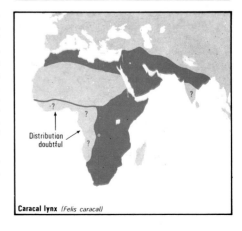
Distribution doubtful

Caracal lynx *(Felis caracal)*

Cardinal

A familiar garden songbird of North America, the cardinal is also known as the 'red bird'. Apart from a black 'bib', the plumage is a mixture of shades of scarlet, that of the female being rather dull due to tinges of brown. Cardinals are finches, about 9 in. long, with a stout beak, a conspicuous crest in both sexes and short, rounded wings.

The range of the cardinal extends from the temperate zone of the United States south to Mexico and British Honduras. It has been introduced to Bermuda and Hawaii. In the latter, it breeds all the year round and has become a pest because of the damage it does to fruit. Cardinals are also spreading unaided northwards through the United States and are now a fairly common resident around New York and in neighbouring parts of Canada. This spread may, at least in part, be due to the popularity of keeping bird tables to attract birds into gardens and to provide them with a plentiful source of food in winter.

Some cardinals migrate south in winter while others, especially the young birds, stay near the places where they were brought up, in flocks of 6—24. It has been suggested that the practice of putting out food for birds may also be reducing migration. Other species in the United States, and the blackcap in Britain, appear to be tending to stay put in winter.

An American songster

Apart from their gay, red plumage, cardinals are popular birds because of their persistent singing. They perform nearly all the year round and, what is more, the female, as well as the male, sings. So accomplished is the female that it is impossible to distinguish the sexes by song alone.

In Tennessee the clear, whistling song of the male cardinal can be heard in January or February, when the ground is still snow-covered. The female starts singing during March, and cardinal song can be heard throughout the summer and autumn, occasionally as late as November or December.

The song is very varied; made up of combinations of notes that have been described as being like a person calling a dog. One male cardinal was recorded as having 28 songs made up of different combinations of syllables. There is also a very quiet song, called the subsong, which can be heard mainly during the courtship season, from February to April.

The cardinals' habitat ranges from moist to desert. On the arid Marias Islands off Mexico, the birds have to drink early morning dew before it evaporates, and cardinals have been seen drinking from pools formed at the bases of leaves. They prefer to live in open woodland with clearings, or mixed growth at the edges of woods. Suburban gardens are very popular, providing both open ground and trees.

Several broods a year

The song plays an important part in courtship and nesting. As is usual when both sexes sing, both male and female defend the territory. The female drives out intruding females but ignores strange males, which are vigorously repelled by her mate.

The songs of the female invite the male to mate with her or to feed her, and at times both will sing together, either in unison or alternately. The female may sing on the nest while the male sings from a nearby tree. Both these songs are, apparently, signals that lead to the female leaving the nest and being fed by the male.

Nest-building starts in March or April. Sometimes the male helps, while at other times he merely accompanies the female while she flies to and fro collecting weeds, leaves, grasses and rootlets which are woven into a bowl. The nest may be compact and well-lined or a very loose, flimsy structure. The clutch, which is started shortly after the nest is completed, consists of 3 eggs, although 5 have been recorded. Clutches laid later in the season usually have only 2 eggs. Incubation takes 12—13 days, starting when the last egg is laid. The chicks leave the nest when 9—10 days old. During this time both parents feed them. As is often the case with fruit-eating birds, the young are fed on insects, which provide a high protein diet necessary for rapid growth.

There may be 3 or 4 broods during the year. In Tennessee, for example, breeding continues from April to August. Farther south, breeding may continue all the year round. The pair stays together throughout the breeding season and may keep company during the winter. While the female builds a new nest and incubates the next clutch, her mate continues to feed the previous brood, which are finally chased out of the territory when the next brood is hatched.

Young cardinals begin to sing when 3—6 weeks old. At first the song is warbling, not at all like the adult song. Adult phrases are added by the age of 2 months and the full song develops by the next spring.

Cardinals feed on fruit and seeds which they crack with their wedge-shaped bills.

Fishy foster-child

Some years ago a photograph appeared in American newspapers of a cardinal standing on the edge of an ornamental pool and leaning over to drop food into the open mouth of a goldfish that had its head out of the water. The photograph and the accompanying story left no doubt as to the truth of this apparently incredible behaviour, and the reader was left with two problems. Why should the goldfish want to be fed, and why should the cardinal want to feed it?

When the behaviour of a bird feeding its chicks is examined a possible cause comes to light. The parent bird alights beside the nest and the young chicks feel the vibration, and immediately raise their heads and gape, showing off a brilliant pink or yellow mouth that contrasts with the dull colours of the nest and surrounding foliage. The brightly-coloured mouth acts as a signal to the parent as to where to place the food it has brought. This is instinctive; in other words, providing the adult bird is in the stage of the breeding cycle when it has chicks, it will automatically put food into a brightly-coloured hole. Because it is automatic, mistakes are made. A fledgling cuckoo sitting on a branch with its mouth open acts as a super-signal for any small bird passing with food for its family. There are also numerous instances of one kind of bird feeding the young of another kind.

So it is not so surprising to find the cardinal dropping food into the bright mouth of a goldfish. However, there is still the mystery of why the goldfish came to the surface and allowed itself to be fed, and this we may never know. It is not something that can be repeated experimentally as it is not possible to make the goldfish come to the surface, or a cardinal to feed it if it does.

class	**Aves**
order	**Passeriformes**
family	**Emberizidae**
genus & species	*Pyrrhuloxia cardinalis*

JA Hancock: Photo Res

◁ *The cardinal is a popular bird because of its gay red plumage and its persistent singing. Both male and female sing; the male's clear whistling song can be heard when snow is still on the ground.*
▽ *An amazing photograph showing a cardinal feeding goldfish. This behaviour cannot be fully explained; the bird was attracted perhaps by the fish's bright mouth — but why was the fish attracted?*

△ *Fledgling begging for food from male. When 3 weeks old it begins to sing warbling songs.*
▽ *Black-throated cardinal Coccopsis gularis of South American forests.*

Paul Lemmons

John Markham

Cardinal fish

This is the name of many small fishes, usually red or with red in the pattern of the body, that live mainly on coral reefs in tropical seas. A few live in freshwater streams on tropical Pacific islands. All but a few deep-sea forms are shallow-water fishes, usually not more than 4 in. long. The largest are up to 8 in. long and these live in the brackish water of mangrove swamps.

There are great numbers of cardinal fishes, suggesting that they are the mainstay of many predatory fishes. They easily form associations with sedentary animals.

Shelter in a shell

The best-known are two species of 2 in. conchfish of the Caribbean, Florida and Bermuda. These shelter in the large molluscs *(Strombus)* known as conches, resting in the mantle cavity and coming out at night to feed on small crustaceans. Not every conch contains a fish and not every cardinal fish shelters in a conch. Some shelter in sponges, empty conch shells or empty bivalve shells, in fact in any convenient hollow object or cavity.

American scientists studying a Hawaiian species of cardinal fish collected over a thousand specimens from a small area of dead coral. This gives a picture of the conchfish hidden away in all manner of cavities and shelters on the sea-bed by day, and swarming out at night to feed. As it is, the fish is mainly seen when a conch is taken from the sea for food. As the mollusc lies on the bottom of the boat it opens its mantle cavity and out flops the cardinal fish.

A fish's portcullis

One cardinal fish *Siphamia versicolor* of the Nicobar Islands in the Indian Ocean, lives in association with a dark-red sea-urchin. When nothing is happening to disturb the peace, the urchin parts its long spines so that they form pyramid-like clusters, and between these the fish moves, cleaning the sea-urchin's skin. At the slightest alarm, even a shadow falling on the urchin, the spines are spread defensively and the fish shelters among them, usually head-downwards.

At night the fish comes out to feed, but if driven from its sea-urchin host it will swim to another. If this urchin is a different colour the fish will change colour to match that of its new host.

Mouth as a nursery

The breeding habits of the conchfishes are simple. As the female lays her eggs, the male takes them into his mouth and there they remain until they hatch. Sometimes, the males alone hold the eggs, sometimes the females, and in other species both parents may share the duty. There are a few species in which the eggs are picked up by the male only when danger threatens. Some idea of what this mouth-breeding involves can be had from a comparison of two species. The female of one in Australian waters lays eggs ⅛ in. in diameter

△ *Cardinals are usually red in colour.*
▽ *Barred cardinal's striped body breaks its outline — quite an effective camouflage.*

▷ *Pyjama fish* Apogon nemoptera, *only recently discovered in the Pacific Ocean. Like many other cardinals, it is a mouthbreeder.*

and the male holds 150 in his mouth. In a Mediterranean species the eggs are $\frac{1}{50}$ in. in diameter and the male holds 22 000 in his mouth.

In this Mediterranean species the eggs are fertilised inside the female's body and there is a curious inversion in the copulation. The genital papilla of the female is long and she inserts it into the male's body to take the sperm for fertilising her eggs. This form of 'petticoat government' is completed by the male taking over the care of the eggs, as we have seen.

Death-like ruse

Little is known about the enemies of cardinal fishes. Consequently, it is possible to make only the generalization that they must be eaten by many small and medium-sized predatory fishes. This is supported by the behaviour of the brownspot cardinal fish. Animals at the mercy of others often use the tricks which used to be known as shamming dead or feigning injury, but which are now included under the comprehensive title of distraction displays. The 3 in. brownspot, so named from a dark spot above each of its breast fins, flops on one side and gives every appearance of being dead when one tries to catch it.

Useless lamps?

There are many animals and some plants which produce living light. In some there is an obvious advantage, as when the female glowworm shines the light at the tip of her abdomen, so bringing the male to her side. In other instances it is hard to see what purpose is served, as with the fungus which grows inside hollow trees, glowing with a spectral light at certain times of the year.

Some bacteria are luminous, and they present much the same case as the fungus: it is hard to see what purpose is served by it. Coastal fishes that have light-organs are dependent on these bacteria for them, unlike deep-sea fishes which produce their own light. Several cardinal fishes have these light-organs. One of them *Apogon ellioti*, from southeast Asian seas, not only has a population of bacteria, but the gland in which this is located has a reflector. Moreover, the muscles below the gland are translucent and act as a lens. The result is that this small cardinal fish swims about at night with a lamp in its throat. The purpose of this elaborate light-organ is unknown.

More remarkable is the cardinal fish that has in its intestine three such lamps, each containing luminous bacteria and each with its reflector and lens. The absurd part of this story is that these lamps are directed towards the interior of the intestine. Presumably this fish takes only light meals.

class	**Osteichthyes**
order	**Perciformes**
family	**Apogonidae**
genera	***Apogon,*** *others*

Caribou

Although placed in the same species as the reindeer, the caribou of North America are so different from the reindeer of northern Europe in their history and economics, that both are treated under separate headings. Reindeer are regarded as the semi-domesticated animals of Scandinavia and Greenland, while the caribou roam wild in North America and Siberia.

Caribou have longer legs than reindeer. They stand 4—5 ft at the shoulder and weigh up to 700 lb. The coat varies from almost black to nearly white, but most caribou are brownish or greyish with light underparts and rump. In winter they become lighter, appearing more heavily built as fat is laid down, and the hair, consisting of woolly underfur and stiff guard hairs, lengthens. The ears and tail are short and the muzzle is unique, being furry. These are adaptations that reduce the amount of heat being lost from the body in cold weather.

With reindeer, caribou are the only members of the deer family in which both sexes bear antlers, although those of the females do not reach the large size attained by the males, who also have a 'ruff' of long hair on the throat.

Migrating herds wear snowshoes

It has been estimated that at the turn of the century 1¾ million caribou roamed the barren grounds of northern Canada, between the Mackenzie River and Hudson's Bay, from Victoria Island in the north almost to Lake Winnipeg in the south. This is a region of generally flat country with many lakes and bogs. The population is now much reduced through overhunting, destruction of food by forest fires and high mortality in severe weather. Having dropped to 278 900 in 1955, the population has built up to 375 000 through an intensive programme of conservation.

Caribou live in small bands of 5—100 animals or in herds of up to 3 000. There is no organisation or established leader; the groups merely move together and close on each other when alarmed.

In April and May the herds migrate north to the open tundra, where they live all summer until June and July, when there is a movement back to the wooded parts at the southern end of their range. The migration follows regular paths and the trails become cleared of vegetation and beaten flat over years of use. In September there is a second movement back to the tundra, but not as far as the summer feeding grounds, for the rut. After the rut they move back to the woods for the winter but a few small bands remain in the tundra all winter.

The caribou's large feet help in its long migration over snow, slippery ice and sinking bogs. The two halves of the cloven hoof are very broad and splay out, reducing the pressure on the ground, thereby acting like snowshoes. The pressure exerted on the

CJ Ott: Photo Res

▷ *Male caribou grazing. Reindeer and caribou are the only members of the deer family in which both sexes have antlers.*

△ *Caribou cow on the barren ground of Alaska.*
▽ *Caribou herd in August finding relief from flies by being on a high snow patch.*

CJ Ott: Photo Res

ground is 2 lb/sq in., a very low figure. The moose, for instance, exerts a pressure of 8 lb/sq in. The concave shape of the hooves and the patches of hair on the under-surface give the caribou a good grip on slippery surfaces. During migration, the herds move forward at the rate of about 19 miles a day, but when hard pressed, caribou can gallop short distances at speeds of over 40 mph.

Lichen feeders

In winter, caribou eat lichen, the so-called reindeer moss, and dried grass, which they find by scraping away the snow with their hooves. They also browse on the twigs of willow and aspen. In the summer they browse and graze on a number of plants, such as birch, willow, horse-tails, grasses and sedges. Cast antlers are chewed, no doubt helping to rebuild the body's supply of calcium salts for the growing of new antlers.

Well-timed births

The rut takes place in late October to early November, and the bulls serve the cows indiscriminately, without forming harems. There is aggression only when the bulls come near each other, and any sparring is short-lived.

During the rut, the bulls thrash the undergrowth with a side to side movement of their antlers. This is part of the courtship display and it has recently been suggested that the enlarged brow-tines on the antlers of the bull caribou are an adaptation to protect the eyes while thrashing the stiff stems of bushes. It had previously been thought that these tines were used as snow shovels to uncover food but no one had ever seen them being used in this way.

The young are born in early June, 90% within a fortnight, while the herds are on their spring migration. If they are born too early, they will succumb to bad weather, and if too late they will not have time to develop sufficiently to withstand the next winter. As the herds are migrating, it is also an advantage for the cows to drop their young at the same time so that they all move at the same speed and there is less danger of stragglers being left behind, where the wolves will be waiting to make an easy kill. Any sick, old, or very young, or those caribou that are separated from the herd are 'culled' by the wolves.

The calves weigh 9 lb when born and can run when half an hour old, and in 4 hours they can outrun a human. This is very necessary, as the mother and calf must keep up with the herd. To encourage the calf to follow her, the cow faces it and bobs her head, grunting at the same time. This always seems to stimulate the calf to follow her. Generally, the cows sort themselves into small bands, each made up of cows with calves of roughly the same age, so that they can run together at the same speed.

When very young, the calves will follow any moving object, so when the band is disturbed the calves follow blindly. When the danger is past, their mothers sort them out, identifying their own calves by scent. By the end of their first month the calves begin to graze, but they will continue to suck throughout the winter.

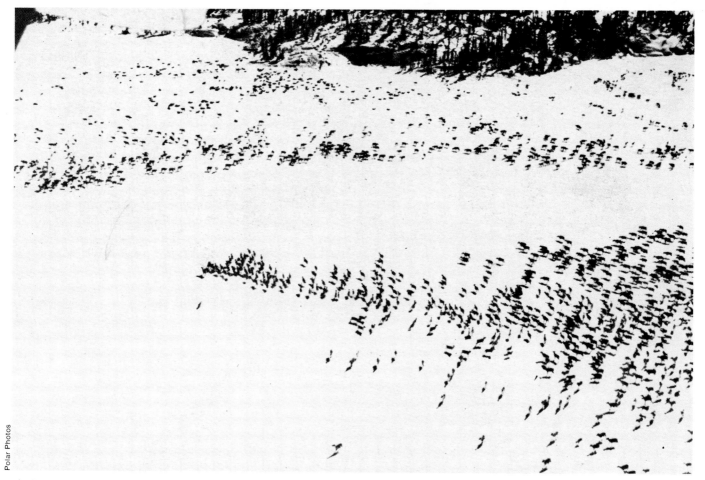

Wolves follow herd

Grizzly bears sometimes prey on young caribou, otherwise wolves are the main enemy. Groups of wolves will associate with the caribou herds for most of the year, preying on sick, old or very young animals, or any that become separated from the herd. It has been calculated that not more than 5% of the caribou population succumb to wolves. One herd of 100 000 caribou was seen to be followed by 20 wolves, with 100 ravens and 3 eagles feeding on carrion.

Provider of all

The caribou were once the northern equivalent of the bison of the North American plains, providing man with nearly all his basic needs. Both animals once existed in vast herds that represented an apparently endless source of food, clothing, housing material and raw material for many implements. The two peoples dependent on the caribou were the Athabascan Indians and the Eskimos. One of the tribes of Indians, living around the Great Bear Lake, were so dependent on caribou that they were called the 'Caribou Eaters'. Eskimo economy was mainly based on the sea, but in summer they would travel inland after caribou. Some small groups of Indians and Eskimos, perhaps numbering 25 000, are still dependent on caribou.

The Indians knew the migration trails of the caribou and would wait for the herds to pass, drive them into corrals and slaughter them. They would also attack the herds as they crossed rivers, for although caribou are strong and swift swimmers, it was possible to intercept them with canoes and spear them. Unfortunately for the Indians the caribou herds sometimes changed their route and so the hunters starved. The caribou were so useful that, when white men started to kill them off, the Eskimos starved. To help them, some 1 300 Eurasian reindeer were introduced in 1891-1902, which bred so well the caribou were crowded out of their range. The tragedy was that the Eskimos showed little interest in the smaller reindeer.

The main use for the carcase is the hide. The complete Eskimo winter outfit consists of an inner and outer suit, for which 12 caribou skins might be needed. Leather from the bull's forehead is used for the soles of boots and calf skins for stockings and the inner suit. Five or six hides make one sleeping bag and 12 skins cover a kayak. Fat is rendered down for use in oil lamps and antlers are used for a number of purposes. They are used for tent pegs, to make chairs and tool handles, while in one part of Canada they have been used as sledge brakes. An antler is fastened upside-down on the back of the sledge and when the driver puts his weight on it the tines dig into the snow.

class	**Mammalia**
order	**Artiodactyla**
family	**Cervidae**
genus & species	***Rangifer tarandus***

△ *A remarkable aerial photograph showing a wolf approaching caribou before singling out one to kill. This huge herd, of which only a minute corner is seen here, was estimated to number 100 000 animals.*

▽ *The Eskimo depends on the caribou for many things. Hide, the bull's forehead, fat and antlers are all adapted for the Eskimo's needs.*

Jane Burton: Photo Res

Carp

Of the extensive carp family (Cyprinidae), this is the most widely distributed. Native of Japan, China and Central Asia, from Turkestan to the Black Sea, it has been introduced into many European countries, including the British Isles, as well as the United States. It differs from other members of the family in its unusually long dorsal fin, with 17−22 branched rays, the strongly serrated third spine of the dorsal and anal fins, and in its four barbels, two at each corner of the slightly protrusible mouth. There are no teeth in the mouth, but there are throat-teeth. The colour of the wild form is olive to yellow-green on the back, greenish-yellow to bronze-yellow on the flanks, and underparts yellowish. The fins are grey-green to brown, sometimes slightly reddish.

Wild carp at home

Carp prefer shallow sunny waters with a muddy bottom and abundant water plants. They avoid clear, swift-flowing, shaded or cold waters. Wild carp are found today mainly in the large rivers. Their food is insect larvae, freshwater shrimps and other crustaceans, worms and snails, as well as some plant matter. The barbels, organs of touch, and the protrusible mouth are used for grubbing in the mud, much of which is swallowed and later ejected when the edible parts have been digested. In winter feeding ceases and the fish enter a resting period, a form of hibernation. In May to June carp move into shallow water to spawn, the eggs laid on the leaves of water plants. Each lays over 60 000 eggs/lb of her body-weight. The larvae hatch out in 2−3 days, the adults return to deeper water, while the young fishes remain in shallow water, near the bank. They become sexually mature in 3−4 years. Small carp will be eaten by almost any fish significantly larger than themselves, including larger carp.

Domesticated varieties

As with many other domesticated animals, carp are found in a number of varieties, of two main types: leather carp and mirror carp. The first is scaleless, the second has large scales in two rows on each side of the body. Both can throw back to the original carp form. The shape of the body varies, from relatively slender to deep-bodied with a humpback. Some fish culturists claim these vary with the food, sparse feeding producing the slender forms, abundant feeding giving rise to humpbacks.

How old is a carp

Carp have probably been domesticated for many centuries, and have been carried all over the world for ornamental ponds, or for food. Surprisingly, therefore, in view of the familiarity that should have resulted from this, there is a conflict of opinion on important points — for instance, their longevity and maximum weights. Above all, there are serious discrepancies about when carp were introduced into England.

△ *Cyprinid fishes, for instance roach, tench and some carp, often show red forms which breed true to type. Aquarists take advantage, with results like these Japanese Hi-goi, golden carps.*

Gesner, the 16th-century Swiss naturalist, mentioned a carp 150 years old. Carp in the lakes of Fontainbleau have been credited with ages of up to 400 years. Bingley, writing in 1805, records a carp in the pond in the garden of Emmanuel College, Cambridge, that had been an inhabitant more than 70 years. Tate Regan, authority on fishes in Britain in the first half of this century, was of the opinion that under artificial conditions a carp may attain 50 years but that 15 years would probably be the maximum in the wild state.

Perhaps one reason for the excessive claims is their hardiness when removed from water. This is also the reason why the fish could be spread over such a wide area by man. Wrapped in damp moss or water plants, it can survive transport over long distances. If Pennant is to be believed, this remark has the force of under-statement. In his *British Zoology* he tells of a carp wrapped in moss, with only its mouth exposed, placed in a net and hung in a cellar. It was fed with bread and milk and lived over a fortnight. It is only fair to add that it was 'often plunged in water'.

Carp usually grow to about 25 lb in Britain but on the continent a fish of over 60 lb and a length of 40 in. has been recorded. Claims have been made for 400 lb carp. Frederick II of Prussia is said to have caught one of 76 lb and a 140 lb carp is said to have

515

E Lindsey

△ *Clarissa, the largest carp caught in Great Britain, was taken from Redmere Pool by R Walker in 1952. She was about 15 years old and weighed 44lb and still lives in the London Zoo's aquarium.*

G Kinns

△ *The mirror carp is identified by rows of large scales along its back and sides.*

▽ *Some think carp found in Britain today came from carp cultivated in monastery stewponds.*

Mansell

been caught at Frankfurt on Oder. There are several records of carp around 25 lb in this country, but there is one for 44 lb taken by R Walker in 1952.

Historical uncertainty

The introduced form of the common carp was known to the Greeks and Romans, and has long been kept in ponds in parts of Europe. We know it is today found widely over England, the southern parts of Wales and in southern Scotland. The question remains: when was it first introduced into Britain?

Writers on the subject seem to have been fairly unanimous that all our carp must be regarded as descendants of fishes cultivated by the monks for centuries in their stewponds. Certainly, carp are still to be found in many of the surviving stewponds adjacent to ruins of monasteries and priories. That on its own is very little help in finding the date when they were first put there. Other than this, information comes from documentary evidence or guesswork, or a mixture of the two.

Eric Taverner, in his *Freshwater Fishes of the British Isles* (1957), suggested that carp were brought here from France and the Low Countries in the 14th century. Richard Fitter, writing in 1959, invokes an entry in *The Boke of St Albans* for dating their introduction prior to 1486. Emma Phipson, in *The Animal-Lore of Shakespeare's Time* (1883), speaks of Leonard Mascall, a Sussex gentleman, who has had the credit for importing the carp into England about the year 1514. She also points out that in the Privy Purse Expenses of Elizabeth of York, 1502, mention is made of a reward paid for the present of a carp. Izaak Walton, in *The Compleat Angler*, opined that the date was around 1530. Dr Albert Gunther, celebrated authority on fishes in the last half of the 19th century, fixed the date at 1614.

The latest pronouncement is by Günther Sterba, in his *Freshwater Fishes of the World* (1962), that the carp reached England in 1512, Denmark in 1560, Prussia 1585, St Petersburg (Leningrad) 1729, and North America (California) 1872.

The dissolution of the monasteries began in 1535. A plan of a Benedictine monastery of the 12th century shows the site of a fishpond. Accepting the dates quoted here the fishponds of religious houses in England must have been stocked for at least two centuries with fish other than carp. Two of our seven authorities give dates about or after the dissolution of the monasteries, and three give dates only slightly before that event.

It is a romantic idea that English monks could supply themselves with carp to be eaten on fast days. But the evidence seems to be in favour of some other fish, probably the perch.

class	**Osteichthyes**
order	**Cypriniformes**
family	**Cyprinidae**
genus & species	*Cyprinus carpio*

Cassowary

These large impressive and flightless birds live in dense rain forests on New Guinea, its adjacent islands and the northeastern seaboard of Queensland. Their drooping black plumage is made of coarse bristle-like feathers. The skin of neck and head is naked and brightly coloured, ornamented with coloured wattles except in the dwarf cassowary, the colours being red, blue, purple, green and yellow. The head is crowned by a bony helmet or casque. The long strong legs bear three toes, the innermost of which has a particularly long stout claw. The wings are very small and hidden. The feathers, owing to the length of the aftershaft (the small tuft at the base of the vane) seem to be double. The quills of the wing feathers are without vanes. But the shafts of the wing feathers remain as horny spines up to 15 in. long. There are three species of cassowary, the Australian, one-wattled and dwarf cassowaries.

Fast forest runner

The largest, the one-wattled cassowary, may be nearly 6 ft tall and weigh up to 150 lb. In spite of their size, cassowaries are seldom seen, as they are shy and secretive, skulking in dense jungle or rapidly making for cover if surprised in the open. They are more often heard, their call being a deep booming or croaking. They can run at 30 mph even through dense thorny undergrowth, with the head down and forward, protected by the bony casque. The stout wing quills, held out and curving to the line of the body, ward off thorns and entangling vines alike. Moreover, they have regular tunnel-like runs through the vegetation. Cassowaries can leap obstacles, plunge into water and swim rivers, and in defence can leap high to make' raking blows with their long dagger-like claws.

The most studied of the three species, the Australian cassowary, goes about singly or in pairs, and occasionally up to six may be seen together. The birds rest during the hottest part of the day in sunny places, which they visit regularly.

Mainly fruit-eaters

The food of the Australian cassowary includes palm seeds, knocked down by fruit pigeons, plums, figs, and other wild fruit and berries, eaten largely during early morning and late afternoon. The food of the other species seems to be similar but includes insects and leaves.

Father knows best

The female is larger than the male, but he is responsible for the care of the offspring. On a nest of leaves at the base of a tree, during June—August, the female lays 3—6 greenish eggs, each about 5 in. long. The male incubates them and guards the chicks, for a total of 7 weeks. During this time, if disturbed, he races away in what must be assumed to be an effort to draw the intruder away. He is conspicuous, the eggs are the

Barry Driscoll

Van Nostrand

▽ *Baby cassowary 48 hours old. The parent's bony casque or helmet protects the head.*

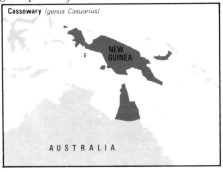

△ *Bennett's cassowary lacks wattles but has great splashes of cobalt blue on the naked neck.*

colour of the leaves they lie on. The chicks are buff with brown stripes.

Pets, with a difference

As so often happens, the main enemy is man, who has hunted the cassowary for its flesh and feathers for centuries. The aborigines of New Guinea also keep the chicks as pets, in their villages. As they grow older they are placed in crude cages which give them little room for movement. Some are kept for their plumes, which are regularly plucked. Others are eaten when full-grown.

Unique killer

The cassowary has often been quoted as the only bird that can kill a man at one blow. It does so by jumping up and striking down with the murderous claw on the inner toe of each foot. Yet we know that cassowaries are seldom seen and are always anxious to give man a wide berth. The natural question must be how far the cassowary's reputation is deserved.

Most writers on the subject declare that many natives on the islands of New Guinea, Aru, Ceram, New Britain and Jobi, the Australian islands where the birds occur, have been killed by cassowaries. This is the sort of statistic one learns to mistrust. Roger A Caras, in his book *Dangerous to Man* (1964), tells us that Allied troops in New Guinea, in

the Second World War, were able several times to confirm native reports about the method used by a cassowary to attack. But he says nothing about actual casualties. Zoo keepers agree they are formidable birds to handle, but still there are no confirmed reports of actual casualties.

The only definite case history is supplied by AH Chisholm, in his *Bird Wonders of Australia*. It concerns two brothers, aged 17 and 14, whose dog flushed a cassowary which showed fight 'and was giving the dog a bad time'. The younger brother, rushing to save the dog, received a kick on the leg. The elder brother, joining in the fray, was kicked in the base of the neck, the claw penetrating his jugular vein. He ran towards home for about 200 yd, then collapsed and died.

This is a far cry from assertions that one blow from a cassowary's claw will kill a man.

class	**Aves**
order	**Casuariiformes**
family	**Casuariidae**
genus & species	***Casuarius casuarius*** *Australian cassowary* ***C. unappendiculatus*** *one-wattled cassowary* ***C. bennetti*** *Bennett's cassowary*

Cat

A typical short-haired domestic cat is about 2½ ft long, including a 9 in. tapering tail which, unlike that of the wild cat, is held horizontally when walking. The weight varies considerably, up to 21 lb being recorded. The claws are retractile and are kept in condition on a scratching post. They are used in climbing, and cats readily climb shrubs and trees to escape persecution (from dogs particularly), to rob birds' nests, or to lie along branches to bask in the sun. The muzzle is well-whiskered and the whiskers are used to feel the way in the dark.

The coat colour varies. The most common, the tabby, is of two kinds. One has narrow vertical stripes on the body, similar to those of the bush cat and European wild cat. The other is nearly the same colour, but consists of broad, mainly longitudinal dark lines and blotches on a light ground. In extreme cases, the dark markings are relatively few, strongly drawn, and stand out conspicuously against the lighter background. Such cats are recurrent mutants that parallel the king cheetah.

The names given to cats indicate some of the colour varieties: ginger, marmalade, tortoiseshell, blue, silver and the black cat, traditionally linked with witches, and, paradoxically, good luck. The pure white cat is either a dominant white or, if it has pink eyes, a total albino. The dominant white usually has blue eyes, and the popular view is that such cats are deaf.

Deaf white cats

Darwin was one of the first scientists to note that white cats with blue eyes are usually deaf, and in 1965 Dr SK Bosher and Dr CS Hallpike, of the Medical Research Council in London, studied the development of the ear in kittens from deaf white parents. They found that for a few days after birth the kittens' ears were normal, then those of 75% of the kittens began to degenerate, and deafness followed. A few of the remainder retained hearing in both ears, and some were deaf in one ear only.

The hearing of other cats extends beyond the range of the human ear into the higher frequencies. This is why a cat responds more readily to a woman's voice. It probably means, also, that a cat waiting beside a mousehole is hearing the rodents' voices when these are inaudible to our ears.

Cats on the tiles

The voice of a cat is the familiar mewing, with the purr being used to express contentment. When hunting, cats are silent, and their loudest vocalizations, usually referred to as 'yowling', must be too well known to need further description. These excessively discordant sounds indicate that the male, or tom, is seeking to impress the female, usually called a she-cat when of the common or garden breed, and a queen when she is a breeding female of pedigree stock.

Okapia

△ *In Great Britain today it is estimated that about 8½ million domesticated cats are household pets.*
▽ *A cat will readily climb trees to escape persecution, to rob birds' nests or just bask in the sun.*

A Boxall: AFA

518

△ *The distinctive Siamese, the sacred, royal or temple cat of Thailand, is a favoured breed today.*
▽ *Tabby cat asleep in the typical relaxed position shown by most cats — wild and domesticated.*

John Markham

Popperfoto

Domestic cats are sexually mature at 10 months or less, the earliest record being $3\frac{1}{2}$ months. The height of the breeding season is from late December to March but the female may come on heat at intervals of 3−9 days from December to August. She is at her best for breeding purposes from 2−8 years. Males are at their highest potential from 3−8 years. Oestrus (heat) may last up to 21 days and is preceded by 2 or 3 days of excessive playfulness. Gestation is usually 65 days but may vary from 56−68 days. There may be up to 8 kittens in a litter; but 13 are known. Very young mothers have only 1 or 2, and the number drops again as the females approach 8 years.

Kittens are born blind, deaf and only lightly furred. The eyes open between 4−10 days. Milk teeth may appear at 4 days but it may be 5 weeks before all have erupted. Permanent teeth are cut between 4−7 months. Weaning begins at 2 months.

Night hunters
Domestic cats have departed less from their wild ancestors than dogs. Although both are intimate household pets, cats have retained a greater independence and more readily go wild, or feral. Dogs follow their prey mainly by scent and run it down. But cats hunt by sound and sight, stalking with infinite patience and stealth or lying in wait.

Cats are night hunters. Their eyes are protected by an iris diaphragm, used to exclude the bright rays of full daylight, giving a vertical slit pupil. At night, or in full shade by day, as in a room, the diaphragm opens fully, giving a rounded pupil, to take advantage of all possible light. As with most nocturnal animals, the eye has a tapetum, a layer of cells behind the retina which reflects light back across the retina to make the fullest use of it. It is the rays from artificial light at night, reflected back from the tapetum, that cause cats' eyes to glow, or shine in the dark, and to lesser extent this can happen on a starlit night with no extra illumination.

Mixed fortunes of cats
The household or domestic cat has been given the scientific name of *Felis catus*. Although various small cats have been tamed since prehistoric times, the present-day domestic cat seems to have been derived from the cafer cat or bush cat of Africa *F. libyca* perhaps with admixture from the European wild cat *F. sylvestris*. It has had a chequered career: venerated and mummified by the Ancient Egyptians, worshipped by the Norsemen, given legal protection when first introduced into Europe, and persecuted with revolting cruelty in the Middle Ages because of its supposed link with witches.

Many years ago the dried body of a cat with two rats, one held in its mouth, was discovered in the cavity of a wall in a 17th- or 18th-century house in Southwark, London. Evidently, this was associated with a superstition, but precisely what is unknown. It may have been a talisman to keep out rats, but an octogenarian joiner, interviewed in 1960, declared it was the custom when he was a boy always to put the body of a cat and a rat in the wall of a new house 'to keep out the devil'.

The cat's eye

△ *The cat's eyes at night. In dim light the muscles of the iris relax to open the pupils wide to admit as much light as possible.*

△ *The cat's eyes during the day. In daylight certain muscles contract to make the pupils slit-like so not too much light enters.*

In most vertebrates the eyes play a particularly important part in the body's receptor system which provides the central nervous system with precise information about the surrounding conditions. Here the cat's eye, which is similar to most vertebrates, is dealt with in detail to explain this complex organ. Each eye is a hollow sphere embedded in its socket in the skull. The eye has three main layers: a tough, fibrous outer coat—the sclera; a layer inside this containing pigment and blood vessels—the choroid; and an inner lining—the retina which contains the light-sensitive cells, the nerve fibres leading from the retina to form the optic nerve, and nerve cells that connect the receptors and the nerve fibres. At the front of the eye the three layers are modified; the sclera forms the transparent cornea, the choroid forms the iris with an opening, its centre the pupil, and the retina ends just behind the ligaments which suspend the lens. The mechanism by which colour is appreciated is not fully understood. The retina contains two kinds of light-sensitive cells called, according to their shape, rods and cones. Only the cones are sensitive to light from coloured objects and even when present it is not certain that colour can be appreciated. The rods are more responsive to light of low intensity. When any kind of light from an external object enters the eye, the curved surface of the cornea, the lens and the humours, bend or refract the light and focus it so that the points of light from the object produce points of light on the retina. Muscles attached to the suspensory ligaments, by contracting, change the shape of the lens, so enabling the image to be focused accurately on the retina. The image is thrown upside-down, and smaller than the object.

The accuracy of the impression that the brain gains of the image depends on how numerous and closely packed are the light-receiving cells, since each one can only record the presence or absence of a point of light.

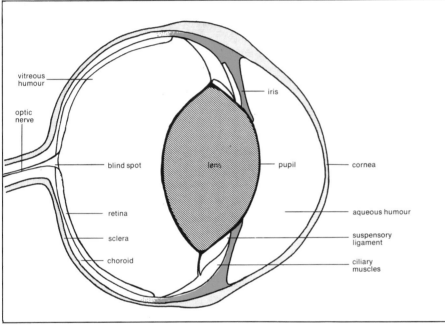

Horizontal section through the eye of a cat. The blind spot is in the region where the nerve fibres leave the eye to enter the optic nerve and there are no light-sensitive cells.

Round pupil as seen in man and monkeys. The radial muscles by contracting make the pupil bigger, the sphincter muscles by contracting make the pupil small so reducing the amount of light entering the eye.

Vertical slit pupil as in the cat. Here, apart from sphincter muscles surrounding the pupil, some cross and are attached to the side. When they contract they have a scissor-like action making the pupil into a vertical slit.

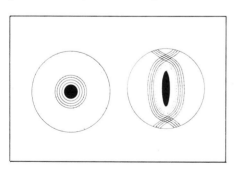

Image formation on the retina shown graphically (corneal refraction ignored). Each eye forms its own image of an object under observation, so two sets of impulses are sent to the brain. Normally the brain correlates these so a single impression of the object is gained. Since each eye 'sees' a slightly different aspect of the same image the combination of these images produce the sensation of solidity and three-dimensional properties of the object. If the eyes are not aligned normally 'double vision' is encountered.

▽ **Cat retina.** *Rods and cones respond to light intensity and colour.*

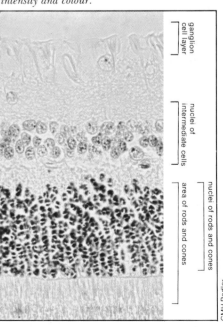

Manx cats and other breeds

There are more than 30 breeds of domestic cat, some long-haired, like the Persian and Angora, but most are short-haired. The majority have long tails, but cats with short tails do occur, especially in southeast Asia. Some are tailless, the Manx cats, and are popularly supposed to be a breed peculiar to the Isle of Man, but probably this breed was originally developed in Japan.

The Manx condition has given rise to strange stories. Occasionally one or more kittens in a litter will be tailless. The story then gets around that the mother had mated with a rabbit or a hare. There have been instances when this story has reached the press, and for a short while accounts of hybrids between a cat and a rabbit create something of a sensation.

In one instance, at least, a litter of four, containing two Manx kittens, belonged to a female domestic cat that had gone wild. The nest was in low undergrowth and all around were rabbits, giving an air of truth to the story, which quickly gained currency locally, that the litter had been sired by a rabbit. Even a fully domesticated pregnant cat tends to seek solitude as the moment of birth approaches. She may even take to woods, where this is possible. In addition, many cats become permanently feral. They are little in evidence as a rule because of the cat's natural wariness, its nocturnal habits and climbing abilities. Also, a cat being a familiar animal, one does not normally stop to enquire whether the cat that disappears into the undergrowth at one's approach is a feral cat, a stray, or a household cat out hunting. Cats have been known to visit woods over a mile away fairly regularly and return to their houses after each hunting expedition.

Feral cats

The ease with which domestic cats become feral was underlined by the story of the Surrey puma. Between August 1964 and November 1967 over 300 people claimed to have seen a puma at large in southern England, the most persistent reports being from the western half of the county of Surrey. Investigation suggested that it was a large feral ginger cat that started the idea. Although feral dogs added to the story, as they did in other southern counties, feral cats were the real instigators and in more than one place the cat was killed and could be measured.

The number of feral cats in Britain, especially in woods on high ground, must be very high. It is usually the larger cats which take themselves off into the wild, but many unwanted cats are taken out into the countryside and abandoned. Such cats seem to grow larger than usual, possibly the result of a more athletic life as well as the abundance of natural food. Mayne Reid, writing in 1889, tells of a domestic cat that went wild and in 4 years doubled in size. The maximum size of which we have records is 42 in. overall, and eye-witness reports suggest that feral cats might attain the maximum dimensions for the wild cat of 45 in. and 30 lb weight.

Their numbers can only be surmised, but the game records for the Penrhyn Estates

△ The mother will often lift and move her young by gently grasping its body in her mouth.
▽ Cat's typical hostile reaction to a dog.

△ Kittens suckling. They are born blind, deaf, and lightly furred. The eyes open at 10 days. Weaning begins about 8 weeks after birth.

▽ A frightened kitten ready to take flight or fight. The hairs are erected, the claws are put out and a threatening posture is shown.

▽ Tommy, a grey-brown tabby, the pet of Mervin Bedell, Long Island, USA, was taught to swim when he was about 4 months old.

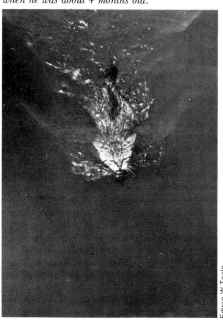

for 1874 to 1902 show that 98 polecats were shot as well as 13 pine martens and 2 310 cats. Even discounting household cats out hunting being shot by keepers, this is an extraordinary figure—one cat per week killed on average, in an area not densely populated by people. While some of these may have been truly wild cats it is fairly certain that many were feral cats and it suggests large-scale breeding in the wild. This is supported by conversations with present-day gamekeepers.

Ferocious cats

In *The Field* for 1871 there is an account showing how readily the tame cat can revert to the wild. It tells of a man who kept a number of tame birds and a cat. For a long time all lived amicably together. Then the cat began to kill the birds, and one day it leapt at its owner, landing on his chest, knocking him over backwards and scratching and biting him as he lay on the ground. His thick overcoat took the brunt of the attack, giving him time to beat off the cat, which ran off and was not seen again.

In breeding it is found that tabby is dominant over black and short hair is dominant over long hair. In practice it is found that feral cats not only achieve a size and ferocity uncommon in tame cats but that all revert to the tabby, whatever the colours of their forbears. All of the well known colour variation in domestic cats has arisen by mutation after they were domesticated.

Outstanding breeds

The long-haired Persian was formerly much sought after, but one of the most favoured breeds today is the Siamese, the sacred, royal or temple cat of Thailand. It was first introduced into England in 1884, and into the United States 10 years later. Related to it is the Burmese, which is probably the older breed, seal brown, with yellow or golden eyes, and without the dark points of the Siamese. Originally reputed to be owned by Burmese aristocracy and priests, each cat had its own servant and could not be bought.

The Abyssinian is probably the nearest to the cats of Ancient Egypt. Grey-brown to reddish in coat, with large, yellow, hazel or green eyes, lithe, with long slender legs and a weak voice, the Abyssinian has come into western Europe in relatively recent times. Its ancestors may well have been those associated with the cat-headed goddess of Ancient Egypt, whose chief seat of worship was the town of Bubastis. Some people claim that 'Puss' is a corruption of 'Bast', but the more likely explanation is that the word is onomatopoeic, in imitation of the cat's hiss. The word came into use first in 1605, when the study of Egyptology was not even in its infancy.

Mummified cats

It is generally accepted that the cat was first domesticated in Ancient Egypt or, if not, that the domestication reached a high peak there. The evidence for this rests on pictures of cats in Egyptian antiquities, and mummified cats deposited in tombs, especi-

Peter Hill

Mary Evans

ally those around Bubastis, during the 2 000 years before the birth of Christ. Many statuettes, figurines and amulets of cats have also been collected from the same sources. That some of these, at least, represent fully domesticated cats can be seen in the tomb paintings of Thebes (1250 BC). In two of these, cats are depicted sitting under a chair, and in one of these the cat is wearing a collar and gnawing a bone.

The mummified cats in particular ought to enable us to decide their wild ancestors, yet this was for a long time in doubt—and for a quite unexpected reason. During the 19th century and the early years of the 20th, mummified cats were excavated in very large numbers and spread over the land as manure. They were also shipped abroad to be converted into fertilizers. One consignment alone, which reached England, contained 19 tons of mummified cats. All that was salvaged from this for study purposes was one skull sent to the British Museum.

In 1907, Professor WM Flinders Petrie, the distinguished Egyptologist, presented a collection of skulls of mummified animals to the British Museum. It consisted of 192 cat, 7 mongoose, 1 fox and 3 dog skulls. They were examined by Mr Oldfield Thomas who

Mansell

Top left: African bush cat, Felis libyca, *hunting. The present day domestic cat seems to have been bred from this species with admixture from the European wild cat,* F. sylvestris.
Top: case for holding the mummy of a cat, which was regarded as sacred in Ancient Egypt.
Left: the black cat has been linked with evil and witches for centuries, but some say it is lucky.

came to no firm conclusion about the cats. Then they were put in store and forgotten. In 1952 they were studied by Dr (now Sir) Terence Morrison-Scott. He concluded, after comparing his results with those of several authors who had examined collections of mummified cats during the 19th and early 20th centuries, that two species were represented. One was the jungle cat *Felis chaus*, the other a form of the African bush cat *Felis libyca*.

From other evidence, it seems that the jungle cat, which is the larger of the two, was not domesticated but foraged around the human settlements. It was only occasionally mummified. The most frequently mummified was the bush cat, but unlike its wild ancestors, judging from the pictures and statuettes, was ginger-coloured, with rather long ears and legs and with a long ringed tail.

class	**Mammalia**
order	**Carnivora**
family	**Felidae**
genus & species	*Felis catus*

Cat-bear

Cat-bear, fox-cat, fire-fox, Himalayan raccoon, red panda are names used to identify this beautiful and appealing carnivore.

The cat-bear is the original panda but the name is now used by popular consent for the larger giant panda. The cat-bear was first made known to western scientists in 1825, nearly 50 years before the giant panda was known to Europeans. It is cat-like in shape, with a 2ft head and body and 22in. brush-like tail. It is one of the most richly coloured of mammals. The body is covered with a rich chestnut, woolly fur, its face is white with a dark stripe from the eye to the corner of the mouth, and the tail is ringed. The underside and the limbs are black and the toes bear long claws that are partially retractile.

The cat-bear is placed in the Procyonidae, the raccoon family, together with the raccoon, the cacomistle, the coati and the kinkajou.

△ The cat-bear or red panda is the nearest living relative of the black and white giant panda.

▽ Its appealing face is white with a dark stripe running from the eye to the corner of the mouth.

The cat-bear, although classified as a flesh eater in the order Carnivora, feeds mainly on leaves and fruit. Here it is eating bamboo leaves.

Mountain forest dweller

The cat-bear spends its time in trees in the mountain forests of Nepal, Sikkim, Yunnan, Szechwan and Upper Burma, at altitudes of 7−12 thousand ft, where it is not uncommon locally. Its day is spent curled up asleep on its side, like a domestic cat, on a branch or in a hollow in a tree. When it comes down to the ground it walks slowly and awkwardly, somewhat pigeon-toed, with the hind feet plantigrade, that is with the whole sole of the foot on the ground as in bears and man. Animals which walk on their toes, as cats and dogs, are known as digitigrade. Certain animals, the hoofed mammals, actually walk on their toenails as seen in horses, giraffes and deer.

If molested the cat-bear hisses and spits like a cat, and occasionally utters a deep growl, like a bear, but is otherwise inoffensive and is readily tamed, although it can give a nasty bite if provoked or carelessly handled.

Vegetarian carnivore

The cat-bear feeds mainly in the early morning and in the evening on leaves and fruit, much of which it forages on the ground. It is said to eat eggs and is reputed to come down to the villages at times to help itself to milk and butter. It is also credited with eating insects, small birds and small mammals, but this is highly doubtful.

Long infancy

Following a gestation of 90 days, two young are born in spring, and these remain with the parents, in a long period of helplessness, until shortly before the next litter is born.

A taste for rosebuds

In 1869 an explorer named Simpson arrived at the London Zoo from Nepal with a somewhat forlorn animal. It was one of three, but two had died on the journey and this third one was weak and ill-nourished. In Nepal this animal is *Nyalyaponga* but Simpson had abbreviated it to *panda*. He told Mr Bartlett, the Director of the Zoo, that he had fed the panda on boiled rice, hay and milk.

Bartlett, looking at the fox-like animal, recognized it as a member of the Carnivora and decided that it needed fresh meat. He told Simpson so in firm terms and explained that this was why the other two had died. Fresh meat was brought, chicken and pigeon, but the panda flatly refused to touch it. Nevertheless, it greedily ate some peas that happened to be lying around, so Bartlett decided to let the animal wander for a while in his garden to see whether it would give some indication as to its likes and dislikes.

The first thing the panda found was some windfall apples. These it ate. Then it tried some leaves and young shoots and finished up on Bartlett's treasured rose-bushes. And that is how the London Zoo's first cat-bear came to be fed on fruit and rose-buds.

Mr Bartlett and Mr Simpson are not the only two people that failed to see eye-to-eye over the panda. The multiplicity of common names with their references to cat, fox, bear and raccoon, show clearly the perplexity over its outward appearance. There is an equal cause for confusion in its anatomy. Its teeth, for example, have much the pattern of a true flesh-eater's teeth.

The incisors and canines are very like those of the true flesh-eaters and the cheek-teeth bear some resemblance. But whereas the true flesh-eater's molars have sharp cusps for shearing flesh, those of the cat-bear are broad with flattened cusps, more suitable for grinding fibrous vegetation.

In an evolutionary sense, also, the cat-bear is 'out on a limb'. It shares the same ancestor as bears and wolves, a primitive dog-like carnivore *Miacis,* which lived in the Eocene period, some 40 million years ago. From this arose two stocks, one leading to the modern bears, the other to the modern wolves, dogs and foxes. Then, about 20 million years ago, an offshoot from the wolf stock gave rise to the ancestral raccoon, from which the modern raccoons, as well as the cat-bear, or lesser panda, are descended.

class	**Mammalia**
order	**Carnivora**
family	**Procyonidae**
genus & species	*Ailurus fulgens*

Cat-bears are found from Nepal over eastern Himalayas to southwestern China, at altitudes of 7 000 − 12 000 ft.

Catbird

Three widely-differing birds have been given the name catbird. The Australian catbirds are very closely related to the bowerbirds. One of these, the toothbilled catbird or stagemaker, clears an arena on the ground and covers it with fresh leaves, cut with the serrated edge of its bill. The Abyssinian catbird is regarded by different authorities either as a flycatcher or a babbler.

The North American catbird, considered here, is one of the mockingbird family, and is a familiar garden bird in North America. Its name is derived from the cat-like mewing notes of the song. The head and body are 4½ in. long, with a 2¼ in. tail. The bird is distinguished by its black cap and russet under the base of the tail. In the same family, there is the black catbird, Melanoptila glabrirostris, *of Yucatan, that has a brilliant iridescent black plumage.*

The North American catbird breeds from southern Canada to the northern borders of the states along the edge of the Gulf of Mexico, ranging across from Atlantic to Pacific Oceans. Part of the population stays near the same place all the year round, but most catbirds migrate southwards in autumn to Central America, south to Panama, and the West Indies. Catbirds also breed in Bermuda.

Catbirds in man-made habitat

In countryside untouched by man, catbirds nest in undergrowth at the edges of forests, along streams and marshes or in clumps of shrubs in open country. This preference for 'edge' country, where dense undergrowth borders open space, must have limited the catbird's range and numbers in the days before man invaded the American countryside. Now that vast tracts have been opened up, leaving islands of woodland, the catbird has spread. As the European settlers pushed west, logging and road-building opened up the forests. Then the civilisation that followed brought first the hedgerows and copses associated with farmland, and the parks and gardens of suburban towns where the catbirds could nest in shrubberies. Catbirds are now firmly established as garden birds where their song and mimicking, although not as good as those of the true mockingbirds, have endeared them to householders. Although they nest, and usually sing, from the cover of shrubberies, they become tame and feed around houses.

A diet of insects and fruit

That catbirds are primarily insect-eaters is shown by the thin, pointed bill, typical of insect-eating birds. Many different insects are taken, including weevils, caterpillars, grasshoppers, beetles, bees and wasps. Catbirds, however, are also fruit-eaters, and have sometimes been condemned as pests of grape and blackberry crops, but this is probably seldom serious. The catbirds feed, also, on the fruits and

The catbird has invaded gardens in N America where its mimicking song makes it popular.

berries of a variety of wild and cultivated shrubs, such as privet, alder, and hawthorn. The introduction of cultivated shrubs such as Tartarian honeysuckle, lilac and forsythia has, along with the general cultivation and opening-up of the land, helped the catbirds to increase, as these shrubs provide both food and nesting sites. The catbirds, in their turn, have helped spread these introduced species by scattering the seeds in their droppings.

Nesting in the undergrowth

The males start singing shortly after their return from their winter quarters and courtship and nesting start within a week of the songs being heard. When the pair has formed, a nest site is chosen, usually 2–3 ft into the foliage of a shrub, but sometimes fairly exposed. The male leads the female in the search for a suitable nest site. Flying in front of her, with a piece of nest material in his bill, he flies to a fork in a shrub, singing all the time. The female watches as he proceeds to play about with the scrap of material as if moulding it into a nest, bowing and fluttering his wings at the same time. At this stage the foundations of a nest may be built, then abandoned, while the proper nest is built a short distance away and about 5 or 6 ft from the ground. The nest is made of twigs, grasses, leaves and rootlets. The female does most of the work, the male merely bringing her some of the material.

The clutch consists of 1–6 eggs, usually 3 or 4, and is brooded for about 13 days. The chicks spend about 11 days on the nest

and are then taken some distance away by the parents. They are fed for another 2 weeks. Depending on the weather, 2 or 3 broods may be raised in a season. The chicks are fed on insects or fruit. In the northern part of the range the first brood is fed on insects, while the second is also fed on fruit which is then available.

Nest raiders

The nests of catbirds are raided by many animals. Chickarees, chipmunks, mink and raccoons, among the mammals, and crows especially among the birds are the main predators, except in suburban areas where the nocturnal forays of the domestic cat probably do the most harm. Snakes also destroy catbird nests. Sometimes the parent catbirds will attempt to drive off the marauder by pecking and beating it with their wings.

Cowbirds, that have the same parasitic habits as cuckoos, attempt to lay their eggs in catbird nests, but, even if one manages to evade the catbirds' attacks and lay its eggs, they will later be thrown out.

Squatters take over nests

In nature nothing is ever wasted including nests and burrows which, once abandoned by their original owners, seldom remain unoccupied for long. Caracals and Cape hunting dogs use the burrows of aardvarks and other animals, and burrowing owls, which can dig their own holes, take advantage of those dug by prairie dogs, armadillos, woodchucks and many others. Voles, mice and wasps live in hedgehog nests. In the trees, many birds' nests are put to a new use after the original family has left. Falcons habitually take over the nests of other species, while the grey kestrel *Falco ardosiaceus,* of Africa, actually evicts the hammerhead from its nest.

In a study of the catbird in Michigan, nests were found to be put to a variety of uses by a number of animals. Apart from insects, spiders and other small animals that make their homes in birds' nests, some catbird nests had been used as foundations by white-footed mice *Peromyscus leucopus,* American robins and mourning doves. The mice converted the catbird nests to their own use by chewing the leaves and bark of the material already there into very fine pieces and constructing their own nest within the structure of the original nest, where they raised their young. Squirrels and chipmunks used the nests for occasional rests.

The small mammals, especially the mice, also used catbird nests as food stores. This is a common use for abandoned nests and it is not unusual to find nest bowls filled with berries or nuts and forming the winter hoards of rodents. One nest had been used as a feeding platform by a green heron *Butorides virescens* that was nesting nearby, and contained the remains of crayfish.

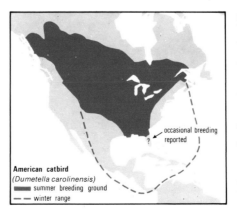

American catbird
(*Dumetella carolinensis*)
■ summer breeding ground
- - - winter range

occasional breeding reported

class	**Aves**
order	**Passeriformes**
family	**Mimidae**
genus & species	***Dumetella carolinensis***

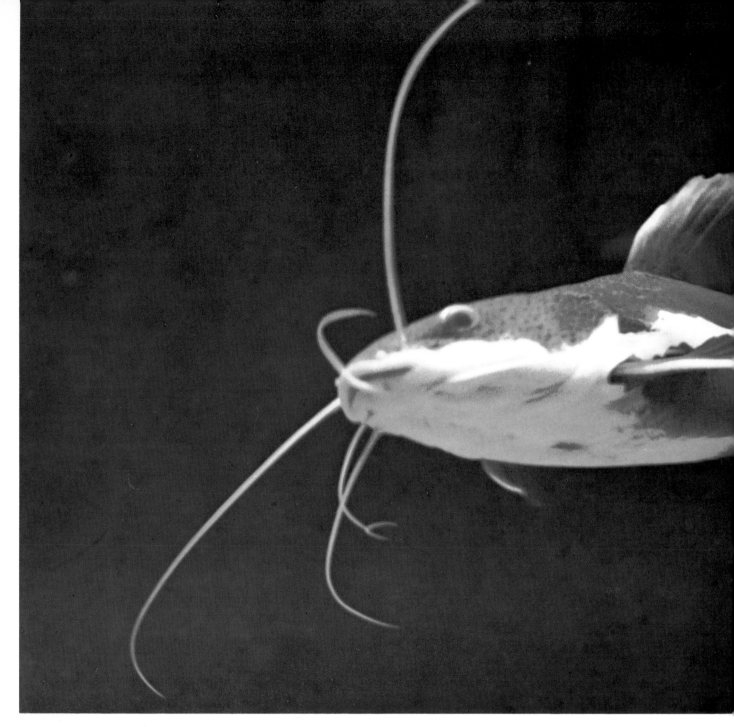

Catfish

The European catfish, or wels, grows to 9 ft or more in the rivers of central and eastern Europe and western Asia, and is the most famous of a large group called the naked catfishes. Its head is large and broad, the mouth has a wide gape and around it are three pairs of barbels or 'whiskers', the feature all catfishes have in common. In the wels one of the three pairs of barbels is very long and can be moved about. The eyes are small. The body is stout, almost cylindrical in front, and flattened from side to side in the rear portion. The skin is slimy and has no scales. The fins, except for the long anal fin, are small. The colour is dark olive-green to bluish-black on the back, the flanks being paler with a reddish sheen, the belly whitish, the whole body being marked with spots and blotches.

The wels has many common names: silurus, the name given it by the Romans, glanis, sheatfish, or sheathfish, said to be from a fanciful resemblance to a sword scabbard, and waller. It has been introduced to a number of lakes in different parts of England.

Night hunter

The European catfish lives in rivers or deep lakes with plenty of water plants. It spends the day under overhanging banks or on the mud in deep water, foraging in the mud with its barbels in search of small invertebrates. At night it hunts, feeding voraciously on fish, crustaceans, and frogs. The larger ones take small water birds and mammals.

In May to June, the breeding season, the catfish moves into shallow water, where the female lays her eggs in a depression in the mud formed by lashing movements of her tail. A large female may lay 100 000 eggs, which are said to be guarded by the male. The fry are black and tadpole-shaped.

Legendary criminal

It would be surprising if a large fish, with hearty appetite, that lurks in dark places did not gather an evil reputation. The wels has been accused of swallowing lambs, even children. Gesner, in the 16th century, reports that a human head and a hand bearing gold rings were taken from the stomach of one of these large catfish.

Good and bad cats

Although related, the various naked catfishes show remarkable diversity in form and habits. The banjo catfishes of South

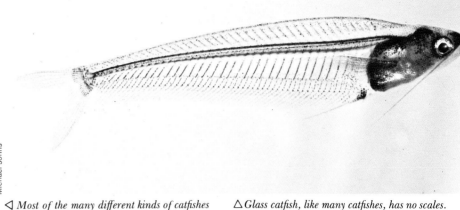

◁ *Most of the many different kinds of catfishes have three pairs of barbels round the mouth.*

△ *Glass catfish, like many catfishes, has no scales.*
▽ *The barbels are used to probe in mud for food.*

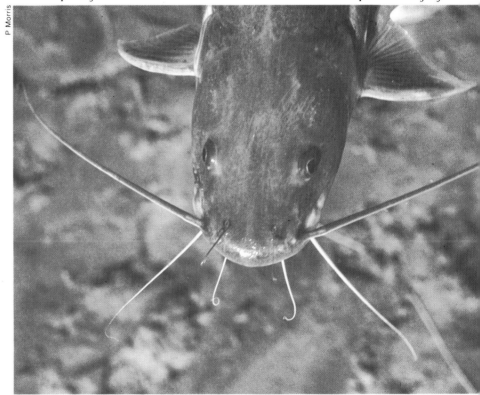

America may live in rivers and brackish estuaries, some species in the sea. They are named for their flattened bodies with an unusually long tail. In one species *Aspredinichthys tibicen* the tail is three times the length of the body. In the breeding season, the females of this species grow a patch of spongy tentacles on the abdomen, and carry their eggs anchored to these.

Marine catfishes of the family Ariidae are mouth-breeders. That is, the male holds the eggs, which in some species are nearly 1 in. diameter, in his mouth, and when they hatch he continues to shelter the fry in the same way. For a month he must fast. Another name for these catfishes is crucifixion fish, because when the skull is cleaned, a fair representation of a crucifix is formed by the bones of the undersurface.

Another family of marine catfishes (Plotosidae) contains one of the most dangerous fishes of the coral reefs. The dorsal and the pectoral fins carry spines equipped with poison glands. Merely to brush the skin against these spines can produce painful wounds.

Equally dangerous are the parasitic catfishes. Some of this family (Trichomycteridae) are free-living but many attach themselves to other fishes using the spines on the gill-covers to hook themselves on, piercing the skin and gorging themselves on the blood. Others insinuate themselves into the gill-cavities, eating the gills. The candiru *Vandellia cirrhosa* is prone to make its way into the urethra of a naked person entering the water, especially, so it seems, if water is passed. A surgical operation may be necessary to remove the fish. Men and women in the unsophisticated areas of Brazil wear a special guard of palm fibres to protect themselves when wading into rivers.

North America has the flathead (family Ictaluridae), a useful catfish reaching 5½ ft long and 100 lb weight. The channel catfish is a most valuable foodfish. There are, however, the madtoms, 5 in. or less, but with pectoral spines and poison glands.

Mad in another sense are the upside-down catfishes of tropical African rivers. From swimming normally these catfishes may suddenly turn and swim upside-down, for no obvious reason. When courting, the male and female upside-down catfishes swim at each other and collide head-on, repeating this at half-minute intervals.

class	**Osteichthyes**
order	**Siluriformes**
family	**Siluridae**
genus & species	***Silurus glanis*** *European catfish others*

527

Holohalaelurus regani
skamoog or shy eye

Catsharks and dogfishes
The best known of the catshark family are the dogfishes, dissected in biology classes all over the world. This catshark is much less well known but has the engaging habit of covering its eyes with its tail when caught, hence its common name: shy eye.

Malcolm McGregor

Catshark

A shark of the family Scyliorhinidae which contains many species, distinguished by the picturesque patterns of stripes, bars and mottlings of so many of its members. One species, a South African skaamoog, is covered with markings that look like Egyptian hieroglyphics. The well-known dogfishes form part of the catshark family. It is better to deal with catsharks as a family, separately from the widespread and thoroughly well-known members, the dog-fishes, if only because two of them are very interesting types of sharks usually wholly ignored in books on fishes. The first of these is the skaamoog or shy eye of South Africa, the second the swell sharks, which are widely distributed in the seas off the Pacific coast of America (from California to Chile), Japan, South Africa, Australia and New Zealand. The family also contains 13 species of deep-water sharks, Apristurus.

There is a related family of false cat-sharks, the Pseudotriakidae, which also live in deep water. One species lives in depths of 1 000 – 5 000 ft in the Atlantic, the other off Japan. These are up to 10 ft long, have an unusually long dorsal fin, but relatively few specimens have ever been seen.

Shy sharks and swell sharks

The catsharks have two dorsal fins and the upper lobe of the tail is horizontal, not uptilted in the usual shark fashion; there is no nictitating membrane (third eyelid) to the eye. This last feature may be linked with the unusual behaviour of the skaamoogs which, when caught, curl their tails over their heads, as if trying to hide their eyes, whence their alternative name 'shy sharks'.

The six species of swell sharks are better-known, especially the Californian species. They are small with broad bodies not more than 4 ft long, and live in shallow seas, especially in beds of kelp. They have large mouths with a formidable set of teeth, but their prey is small fishes, although they probably take carrion since they often find their way into lobster traps.

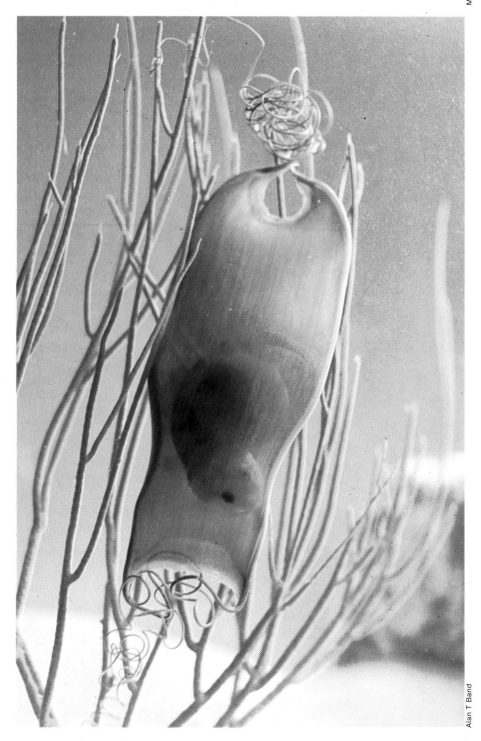

Alan T Band

▷ *Fins of fishes are generally used for stability and steering rather than for swimming. The force which most fishes use to move through the water comes from the blocks of muscles in the body and tail running down each side of the backbone. When a muscle block contracts it bends the body. As each block contracts after the one in front (while the one on the opposite side relaxes) waves transmit a backward momentum to the water which, by action and reaction, makes the fish move forward.*

▽ *The mermaid's purse is the egg case of certain sharks and skates. On the left below an embryo swell shark, still attached to its yolk sac, can be seen developing inside the horny egg case. The entwining tendrils anchor the case until the young shark is ready to hatch (below right).*

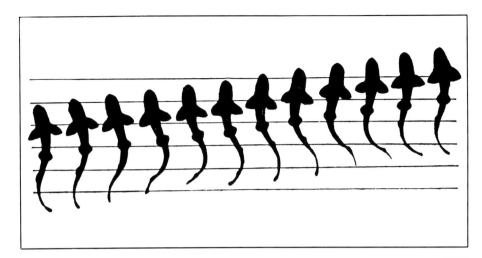

Birth of a shark

All members of the family have similar breeding habits. Fertilisation is internal and the female lays eggs enclosed in rectangular, translucent horny cases with a long tendril at each corner. The tendrils become entangled with such things as the branches of soft corals (sea fans) and are anchored for the 8 months (in swell sharks) during which the embryo is developing, feeding on the large supply of yolk contained in the egg. At the end of this time the developing baby shark, which has been, during the later stages, rotating slowly and spasmodically within the horny case, breaks out at one end.

Puffed up without pride

Swell sharks are named for their most distinctive feature. When hauled out of water they swell up to twice their normal diameter. This is due to their swallowing air, causing the stomach to swell like a balloon. When a swollen shark is thrown back into the water it is likely to float until it can discharge the air. The time taken to do this varies.

Some will deflate fairly quickly and then swim to the bottom. Others may take as long as 4 days, during which time they float.

Normally no shark leaves the water voluntarily and any intake will be of water, which would not put the fish at the same disadvantage as a stomach full of air. Presumably this is some form of defence mechanism, although how it helps is hard to see. Without stressing the analogy it is tempting to recall how general is the habit of inflating the body among toads. The two processes have probably arisen separately, and yet there is a further comparison to be made. The common frog of Europe will at times, when handled, go into a kind of catalepsy, holding its body rigid and somewhat flattened. Its limbs also are held rigid, with the forefeet over its eyes, rather as the shy-eye sharks cover the eyes with the tail.

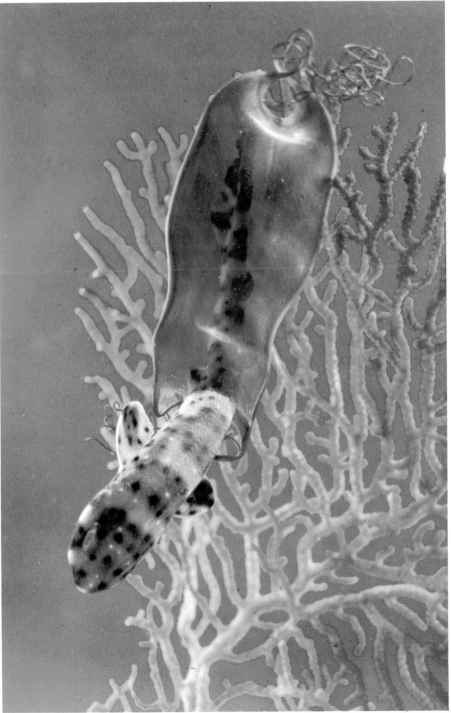

class	**Chondrichthyes**
order	**Lamniformes**
family	**Scyliorhinidae**
genera & species	***Cephaloscyllium uter*** *Californian swell shark* ***Holohalaelurus regani*** *shy eye others*

Cattle

Two species of large hollow-horned ruminants, belonging to the family Bovidae, are called cattle. The name, from the Latin for 'head' indicates property, and meant originally much the same as 'capital' and 'chattel', words having the same origin. Although we sometimes speak of wild cattle this is a contradiction. Strictly speaking, cattle must be domesticated, and the two species are the western cattle (dealt with here) and the zebu of southern Asia and Africa.

Western cattle were derived from the aurochs, Bos primigenius, *which once lived in the forests of Europe and Asia and became extinct in 1627, the last survivor dying in a Polish park. The bull stood 6½ ft at the shoulder, with long curving horns. Its coat was black with a white stripe down the middle of the back, with white curly hair between the horns and white or greyish muzzle. The cows were smaller, brownish-red with some black or fawn patches. The calves were red.*

The colour, size and shape of horns varied from one part of the range to another, and this is reflected in the types of cattle seen over Europe today.

The date and place of the first domestication are unknown. By 2500 BC several distinct domesticated breeds were already in existence. For example, Egyptian drawings of that date show a hornless breed, as well as long-horned and short-horned cattle.

Invaders bring their own cattle

While prehistoric man was still a hunter, he killed the aurochs for its meat and hide. When it was domesticated he could get milk from it as well, and as man became a farmer, he could use it for pulling the plough. British cattle, like the British themselves, are of mixed ancestry, arising from different strains coming in from continental Europe. In settlements of Bronze Age and Iron Age people have been found remains of long-faced cattle, smaller than aurochs and with shorter horns. These are *Bos longifrons*, also called Celtic shorthorns. Later, the Romans brought in their own cattle, larger than the Celtic, with white coats, some with long horns and, probably some hornless. These, it is thought, were the ancestors of the English white park cattle, which include herds such as the Chillingham and the Chartley.

The Anglo-Saxons brought red cattle, larger than the Celtic, and these became established more especially in southern and eastern England, and there was a marked division for a long time. In the 17th century for example, there were mainly all-black cattle in the north of England, the Midlands and in Wales, reflected today in the Welsh Black, Aberdeen Angus, and others. The Danes brought dun-coloured, hornless cattle, the Normans nothing new, but in the 16th to 18th centuries Dutch cattle were imported. These had broken colours, black and white and red and white.

Resurrecting the aurochs

The various breeds of cattle in Britain today reflect these admixtures, in their colours as in their names. Other breeds on the continent of Europe also tell of the course of events there. Some of this is contained in the account of experiments carried out in Germany aimed at 'resurrecting' the aurochs by breeding back.

In 1921 it occurred to Lutz and Heinz Heck that it might be possible to cross selected modern breeds of cattle to reconstruct their wild ancestor. Heinz Heck, director of the Munich Zoo, crossed Hungarian and Podolian (SW Russia) steppe cattle, Scottish Highland, Friesian and Corsican cattle and several grey and brown Alpine breeds. After some years he obtained a bull and a cow both of which had the characteristics of the aurochs, and these two bred true to type.

Lutz Heck, at the Zoological Gardens in Berlin, used Spanish fighting cattle, Corsican and Camargue cattle and English park cattle. These seem to be closer to the aurochs in type and he obtained quicker results. His stock in Berlin was lost during the Second World War although some of his specimens, sent to other zoos, survived.

The reconstituted aurochs not only had the physical characters of the wild ancestor but also its agility and wildness. It is of interest to recall in this connection that bones from Neolithic settlements, through the Bronze and Iron Ages, show that domesticated cattle decreased in size until the Iron Age, and then increased again until modern times. The original diminution in size may have been due to deliberate selection of less agile and less wild individuals, for in domestication, docility is preferable to aggressiveness and a marked agility makes for difficulty in control. Once these two ends were achieved later selection could be profitably directed towards increase in size.

Cattle ask to be domesticated

Two factors which made domestication of cattle relatively easy are their social nature and ability to do well on a wide variety of foods. Cattle naturally live in groups, or herds, which means they readily form social bonds with others of their kind. They also live readily with individuals of other species, which makes it easy for them to live in association with man.

The aurochs was widely distributed over Europe and Asia, which indicates a species ready to adapt to a wide range of climate and to accept a diversity of food plants. Both these were important in the early years of domestication, and also in the spread of cattle by humans to all parts of the world.

The whole process of domestication is so sophisticated that one is constantly surprised that primitive peoples should have accomplished it. Their knowledge of natural history may have been rule-of-thumb, but it was none the less profound. For example, primitive peoples today dealing with semi-wild cows quickly learn that the sight of a calf, or of a boy dressed in a calf skin, will cause the let-down of milk in an otherwise refractory cow. Moreover, in the absence of these the let-down can be stimulated through inflating the cow's vagina by blowing air into it. This gives the animal a stimulus similar to that when a calf is born. The gestation period varies with the breed and may be as little as 270 days or as much as 439 days.

Versatile cattle

The use to which cattle are put has varied at different times and still varies in different countries.

Farmers usually divide cattle breeds into three types: beef, dairy and dual-purpose. In Britain they may be grouped respectively: beef – Shorthorn, Devon, Sussex, Hereford, Aberdeen Angus, Galloway, Belted Galloway, Highland; dual-purpose – Ayrshire, Friesian, Kerry, Jersey, Guernsey; dairy – Shorthorn, Lincoln Red Shorthorn, South Devon, Red Poll, Welsh Black, Dexter.

Beef cattle are primarily intended for meat production and their milk yield is of secondary importance. A good beef animal is deep, thickly and evenly fleshed, and blocky in appearance. In some parts of the world – for example, the La Plata river basin of South America and the western ranges of the United States – beef animals predominate. This is because they are well adapted to sparse grazing and can be farmed in arid areas. They may also be kept to convert surplus corn to protein.

A good dairy cow has a more angular shape, lighter in the fore-quarters and widening out backwards to give a wedge shape. Backbone and hips are less well fleshed but the chest is wide and deep, and the udders are well developed. The average milk yield of a British Friesian cow is 900 gallons in one lactation; many cows give over 20 000 lb of milk a year, and some give over 30 000 lb.

In western societies, milk, meat and leather, in that order, are the desired products. In some less sophisticated societies today none of these is important. In one place the dung may be valuable as fuel, or as a building material. In another place cattle may be kept for their meat and for sacrificial purposes. The Masai of East Africa drink the blood of their cattle, periodically bleeding them for this purpose. Leather may once have ranked first, for covering shields or for body armour. The bulls have been used for sport, and secondarily for meat, in times as far apart as Ancient Crete, the home of the mythical Minotaur, and modern Spain.

It seems highly likely that in the early days of domestication and, in some countries, persisting even to this day, the primary use of cattle was as draught animals, for pulling carts and ploughs. In parts of Africa they are an index of wealth, a means of purchasing wives – cattle or chattels in the original sense of the word.

▷ *Highland cattle keeping cool.*

class	**Mammalia**
order	**Artiodactyla**
family	**Bovidae**
genus & species	***Bos taurus*** *western cattle*

This remarkable fresco is to be found in caves at Jabbarren in the Sahara desert which must once have been fertile cattle country. It was painted on a rock-face away from any shelter. The oxen belong to two species; one with delicate horns more or less curved into the shape of a lyre must represent the African ox, Bos africanus, and another with thick horns, seen in this painting with horns projected forwards, Bos brachyceros, the thick-horned ox. In the foreground of the marching beasts an animal has been killed and one of its legs has already been cut off indicating that primitive men farmed these semi-domesticated cattle.

Aurochs, the wild ox of Europe and Asia, died out in 1627. It stood 6½ ft at the shoulder and the many modern breeds are descended from it.

Reconstituted aurochs, one of a herd produced in the Munich zoo by several years of interbreeding among modern varieties of cattle.

British Friesian: descended from the famous Dutch dairy breed imported prior to 1892. This is one of the most popular breeds throughout the world.

Guernsey: originated on the island of Guernsey where records show that it has been bred on pure lines for several hundred years.

Hereford: of mixed and obscure ancestry. They were originally used as draught animals and selected for size, strength and vigour.

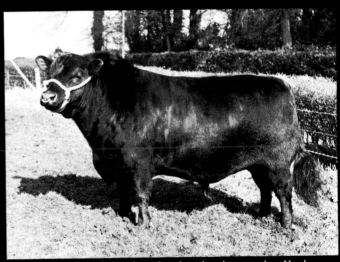

Aberdeen Angus: early breeders selected for hornlessness, then Hugh Watson (1789-1865) took black cattle to Angus and improved the breed.

Dairy Shorthorn: Shorthorns originated in Durham and were improved in the 18th and 19th centuries to give beef or dairy type cattle.

The udder of a prize British Friesian showing the outstanding depth and the development of the milk veins in this supreme dairy cow.

Photographs by: Farmer and Stockbreeder

▽ Swiss cow in a mountain meadow, complete with cowbell (used in herds the world over).

Robin Fletcher

△ A herd of British Friesians, one of the most popular and high-yielding of the dairy breeds.

△ Rarity—a pair of white wild oxen, one of the oldest breeds surviving in Britain at Chartley.

Geoffrey Kinns: AFA

AJ Sutcliffe

the two groups of chromosomes, the former chromatids, undergo changes which result in their eventual disappearance from view; this stage is known as telophase. Finally the cytoplasm of the cell divides into two halves and two new cells are produced each with the same number of chromosomes, the same number as found in the parent cell.

Meiosis

The type of cell division known as meiosis consists of two divisions of the cell with only one division of the chromosomes. Chromosomes are built up of a substance called deoxyribonucleic acid — DNA — and protein. DNA carries within its structure, in units called genes, most of the hereditary information necessary for the development of the individual. The importance of meiosis lies in the way in which genes are exchanged between chromosomes thus creating new combinations of hereditary material during cell division. Meiosis in adult animals is confined to special organs of the body; in the male these are the testes and in the female the ovaries, producing sperm and eggs respectively. Although there are a number of different stages in the production of sperm and eggs only the meiotic division will be described here.

In a cell about to undergo meiosis the chromosomes become visible as single, thin, thread-like structures, often with a beaded appearance. The chromosomes soon begin to pair up two by two, one of the pair being derived from the father of the individual and the other from the mother. The pairs of chromosomes are called homologous chromosomes and they match each other perfectly, gene for gene. The chromosomes of each pair become so closely coiled around each other that they appear as one; the term bivalent is applied to the pair in this condition. Shortly after this the two chromosomes forming the bivalent begin to pull apart and it becomes evident that each chromosome consists of two chromatids making a total of four in each bivalent. The chromosomes of each bivalent are joined at certain points along their length, each point is called a chiasma. The latter represent points of interchange between a chromatid of one chromosome and a chromatid of the other chromosome of the bivalent; chiasmata do not form between chromatids of the same chromosome. Genes are thus exchanged between the chromosomes. Eventually the chiasmata begin to disappear and the bivalents move to the cell centre.

Formation of the spindle as in mitosis marks the beginning of metaphase I. The bivalents become arranged on the spindle at the equator of the cell and anaphase I begins when the chromosomes of each bivalent lose contact with each other and begin to move to opposite poles of the cell, pulled by their centromeres which do not divide. At each pole at telephase I is a group of chromosomes which number only one half that found in the parent cell.

Each of the two telophase cells formed usually immediately enters a second division which is very similar to mitosis. The chromosomes arrange themselves at the equator of the cell in metaphase II, the centromeres divide and the chromatids move to the poles of the cell during anaphase II. Telophase II follows and gradually the chromosomes disappear from view and the cytoplasm becomes divided up between the new cells produced.

Meiosis thus results in the production of four cells, each cell having the halved or haploid number of chromosomes. When haploid sperm and egg unite during fertilisation in a sexually reproducing animal species, the diploid number of chromosomes as found in the ordinary body cells of the animal is restored. This demonstrates the significance of meiosis in that it allows new unions of hereditary material to occur, so that the animal species can best adapt to a constantly changing environment.

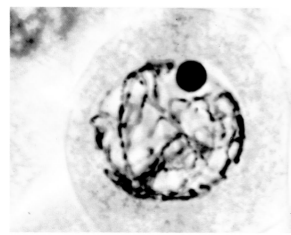

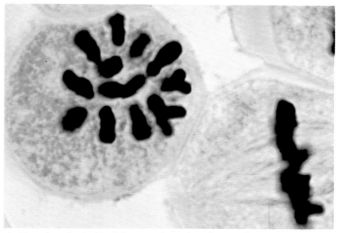

Meiosis in the pollen mother cells of **Lilium** *(× 1 920) demonstrates principles common to plants and animals.* △ *Leptotene: one of several preliminary stages, showing thread-like chromosomes and a nucleolus.*

▽ *Anaphase I: the centromeres do not divide, but the chromosomes of each bivalent part company and are dragged to opposite poles of the cell. This accomplishes the halving of chromosome numbers.*

△ *Metaphase I: the bivalents or pairs of homologous chromosomes are attached by their centromeres to the spindle equator. The cell on the left has been sectioned through the plane of the equator.*

▽ *Telophase I: the chromosomes cluster together but though the cytoplasm is dividing in two no nuclear membrane appears, because a mitotic division will follow immediately, to give four new cells.*

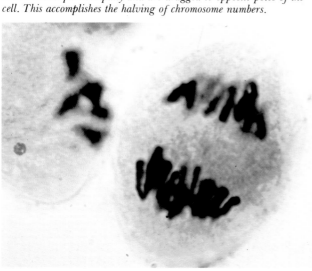

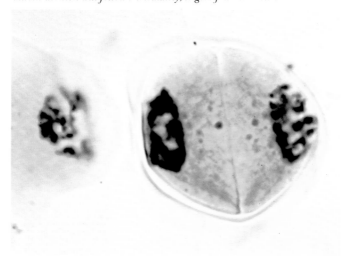

Photos by Gene Cox: Microcolour Int

Centipede

There are many different kinds of centipedes but as they are little noticed and even less liked they do not have common names individually—to most people one centipede is much the same as any other. Scientists, however, have divided them into four orders, the Scolopendromorpha (millipede-like forms), Lithobiomorpha (living-under-stone forms), Geophilomorpha (earth-liking forms), and Scutigeromorpha (shield-covered forms). The first two include the active, elongate but not very slender animals having respectively 21 pairs and 15 pairs of legs. The Geophilomorphs are slender, worm-like centipedes with the pairs of legs varying in number from 31–177, so that some of them more than justify the name 'centipede' or 'hundred-legs'.

The Scutigeromorphs are very distinct and curious. The body is cigar-shaped, not sinuous, and the 15 pairs of legs are very long and slender, enabling the animals to run with remarkable speed and agility. Their respiratory system and the oxygen-carrying capacity of their blood is more efficient than in other centipedes, a feature related to their high rate of activity. Although their appearance is so distinctive, the Scutigeromorphs are allied to the Lithobiomorphs, both orders having 15 pairs of legs.

As there are no common names the scientific (Latin) names must be used. The most familiar British species is Lithobius forficatus, *the dark-brown centipede that scuttles away when a log or a rock is lifted. Another common species,* Lithobius variegatus, *with speckled legs, is unusual in being apparently confined to the British Isles. The long, slender Geophilomorph centipedes are also common in Britain and are most often found when digging the garden. Most of them are only 1 or 2 in. long, but the North African species* Oryza barbarica *may measure up to 7 in. Many of the Geophilomorph centipedes exude a strongly luminous fluid when molested or injured.*

There are only three small Scolopendromorph centipedes in Britain but in the tropics they are very numerous and varied and include giant forms. The tropical American Scolopendra gigantea *may be 1 ft long and the common Asian species* Scolopendra morsitans *reaches 8 in.*

The long-legged Scutigeromorphs occur in southern Europe, the United States and throughout the tropics.

Unwelcome visitors

The body covering of centipedes is not waterproof and they easily die of desiccation. They are confined, therefore, to humid surroundings and are commonly found in leaf mould, compost heaps, under logs and stones, beneath the bark of trees

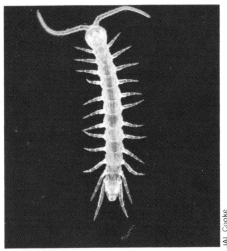

JAL Cooke

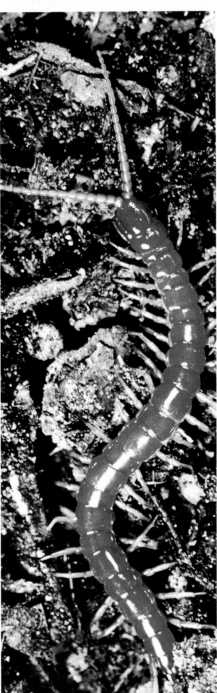

Carolina Biological Supply Co

and in the soil; they come into the open only at night when the air is moist and cool. One British Geophilomorph *Scoliophanes maritimus* lives on the seashore under stones that are covered at high tide. Centipedes often enter houses and a long-legged centipede *Scutigera forceps* found in dwellings in the warm parts of the world, is regarded as beneficial as it preys on insects. In tropical Asia the large and venomous *Scolopendra morsitans* is often found in houses, but is by no means a welcome visitor. Many caves in hot countries harbour centipedes, especially the long-legged Scutigeromorphs, which look quite remarkable in the light of lamps or torches, racing about on the floor and up the walls.

Active hunters

Centipedes are active predators, hunting insects, spiders, worms and other small prey. The common *Lithobius forficatus* readily accepts flies in captivity and a large tropical *Scolopendra* kept for over a year in the London Zoo fed mainly on small mice. In the wild state these large centipedes prey on big insects such as locusts and cockroaches and also on geckos and other nocturnal lizards. The marine centipede *Scoliophanes maritimus* has been seen eating barnacles. Some of the worm-like Geophilomorpha feed partly on plant tissues.

Poisonous legs

The poison bite of centipedes is used to paralyse and kill prey. All centipedes have a venomous bite that is inflicted not by the jaws but by the front pair of legs, which are specially modified as 'poison claws', being hollow and connected to poison glands. The bite of the large tropical Scolopendras is excessively painful and occasionally dangerous, though very few fatalities have been recorded.

Breeding

The sexes are very similar and can usually be distinguished only by microscopic examination. All centipedes lay eggs and in the Lithobiomorpha and Scutigeromorpha when the young hatch they have fewer legs than the adult (7 pairs in *Lithobius*) and they reach the full number in the course of development.

Most centipedes merely lay their eggs in the soil and leave them, but the big Scolopendras brood and guard their eggs and young, fiercely fighting any enemy which attacks, and also protecting them from fungal infection by mouthing and licking them. If seriously disturbed they will often eat the eggs or young, or may desert them, and, unattended, the eggs always go mouldy and die.

Centipedes are long-lived creatures and even the little *Lithobius forficatus* may live for 5 or 6 years. The big tropical species probably take at least 4 years to reach full size and may live for considerably longer.

Well protected from enemies

Small centipedes are readily eaten by birds when exposed by spade or plough but they are well protected from enemies of their own size by their poisonous bite. One Malayan monitor lizard, after dissection, was found to have a stomach almost full of

PH Ward

large *Scolopendra* centipedes. Very few animals, however, have an appetite as robust as this, and these big centipedes must have few enemies. In staged combats they are almost always more than a match for spiders or scorpions of their own size.

See how they run

In the earlier days of zoology, the rapid movements of centipedes made the details of their locomotion something of a puzzle and the only conclusion reached was that if the animal stopped to think about how it should move its legs it would make poor progress. This situation has been celebrated in rhyme:

A centipede was happy, quite
Until a toad in fun
Said, 'Pray which leg goes after which?'
This raised her doubts to such a pitch,
She fell exhausted in the ditch,
Not knowing how to run.

The problem has been resolved by high-speed photography. In most centipedes the legs move rhythmically in waves which alternate on either side of the body, so that in any part, at a given moment, the feet will be bunched on one side and spread on the opposite side. When the legs bunch the tips often cross, but the centipede seems to be immune to the hazard of falling over its own feet. In the long worm-like Geophilomorph centipedes this pattern of movement is not seen; each leg seems to move on its own, picking its way independently of the others. Much of the movement of these centipedes consists of burrowing rather than running, and this sort of leg action is more suitable for such deliberate pushing along of the body.

phylum	**Arthropoda**
class	**Chilopoda**
orders	**Geophilomorpha**
	Lithobiomorpha
	Scolopendromorpha
	Scutigeromorpha

Centipedes paralyse and kill their prey with a venom from poison claws which are developed from the first pair of legs. The giant Malayan centipede (bottom right) may grow to 8 in. long and can inflict a very painful bite which has occasionally killed a human. The tropical American species of Scolopendra, *bottom left, may grow to 1 ft long. The young* Lithobius *centipede (top left) hatched from its egg with only seven pairs of legs. When fully grown it will have 15 pairs. This type is common in Britain and grows to only 1 or 2 in. long but it may live for 5 or 6 years. Centipedes are often confused with millipedes but they may easily be told apart as these pictures show: each segment of a millipede* Polydesmus *(top right) has two legs; centipedes have only one pair to each segment.*

These pictures of different centipedes show how they walk with rhythmic waves of leg movements alternating on either side of the body.

Jane Burton: Photo Res

541

Chaffinch

The chaffinch is a familiar bird in both garden and countryside. It is easily distinguished in flight by a broad white patch on the wings and white streaks on the outer tail feathers. When on the ground or perching, the male chaffinch is seen to be a handsome bird, with slate-blue crown and nape, chestnut back and cheeks and underparts pinkish-brown. The wings and tail are brownish-black, with prominent white wing bars. The female's plumage is not so bright and lacks the slate-blue on the head.

The chaffinch is the most numerous finch in Britain and one of the commonest of all birds. On the continent of Europe, north to the tree-line in Scandinavia and east to Tomsk, the continental chaffinch is widespread. Its cheeks and underparts are a purer pink than those of the British race, with which it mixes from mid-September to mid-November, when large flocks of chaffinches migrate over from the Continent and spread across Britain. Continental chaffinches are also found in Northwest Africa, the Canaries, the Azores and Madeira. They winter in North Africa, Iraq and the Middle East.

Dialect songsters

Outside the breeding season chaffinches become gregarious, forming flocks of several dozen. They fly with the undulating flight typical of finches. The wings are flapped rapidly for a few beats, then closed and the bird loses height, climbing again during the next series of wingbeats. These flocks are readily identified by the flashing white wing bars.

This ganging into flocks is not unusual. Many birds are more sociable outside the breeding season, particularly in hard weather. But even in mild weather chaffinches assemble in flocks, feeding together in the fields and woods and roosting together in shrubberies or hedgerows. Often the chaffinch flocks join other species, and flocks several hundred strong can be seen feeding in the fields. Together with the chaffinches there may be linnets, greenfinches, sparrows and buntings, as well as several kinds of tits and also, on occasion, winter visitors like the brambling.

An unusual feature of chaffinch flocks is that the sexes often form separate flocks. The hen chaffinch is less brightly coloured and therefore less easily detected among a crowd of sparrows or the other small birds in a mixed flock. As a result it was once thought the hens migrated south, leaving the cock chaffinches behind, which earned the cocks the name of bachelor birds.

When in flocks, chaffinches can be heard calling with the familiar metallic 'chink-chink' notes. In the spring the males sing from a favourite perch. The song consists of a succession of musical notes followed by a whistling flourish. In early spring, when the birds are starting to sing the song is shorter, made up of only the first few notes, later it is extended and the flourish is added.

The song varies from district to district, each place having its dialect, which young chaffinches learn by listening to their parents and neighbours.

Horny nut-cracking beak

Chaffinches eat a variety of seeds, fruit and small animals including insects, spiders and earthworms. More plant than animal food is eaten. They take seeds of many plants, including conifers, and fruit such as apples and currants. They also eat blossom and buds but never to the extent of being a serious pest, like their relatives the bullfinches (see p. 436).

The upper half of a finch's bill has a groove down each side, into which the sharp edge of the lower half fits forming a nut-cracker. The conical bill and large jaw muscles are used for cracking seeds and the split seed is turned between the edges of the bill using the tongue to peel the husk.

Woodland breeder

In February the winter flocks break up and the chaffinches move from open country into woodland, where the males establish their territories by singing from favoured perches and chasing intruding males. Females are greeted by an invitation posture, the male approaching her in a lopsided crouch with one leg bent. He then lures her into the territory by singing and displaying.

The female chooses the site for the nest, and builds it, using grass, roots and moss. She decorates the outside with pieces of lichen fastened with spiders' web. Nest-building may take 3–18 days and the chaffinches make, on average, 1 300 collecting trips.

Most of the clutches of 4 or 5, sometimes up to 8, eggs are laid in May, and the female alone incubates them. The chicks hatch after 11 or 14 days and the female continues to brood and feed them by herself. Later the male helps her, but he supplies only 15% of the food. After a fortnight the chicks leave the nest and are led to dense cover in the territory. Here they are fed for about three weeks, then they become more active, flying about the territory and learning to fend for themselves.

Enemies

Chaffinches and other small birds have many enemies. Hawks and owls prey on the adults, while stoats, cats, magpies and jays rob the nests. The behaviour of chaffinches when they see a predator depends on its position. A hawk flying overhead causes them to bolt for cover, where they freeze. On the other hand, a perched owl attracts a crowd of chaffinches and other small birds which gather round it calling loudly. The chaffinches utter a 'chink' call when mobbing an owl. This alerts other birds. When hiding from a hawk, the call is a high, thin 'seet' that makes other chaffinches fly to cover. Unlike the 'chink' call, it is very difficult to tell where the 'seet' call is coming from, so that the caller's hiding place is not disclosed. It is enough to warn the other birds that there is a hawk about. The 'chink' call, on the other hand, tells other birds where the danger is.

Learning by imitation

Poets have attributed to birdsong the expression of pure, irrepressible joy, yet for all its ability to please the human ear, the function of a cock bird's singing is strictly practical: to keep other males out of its territory and to attract females in. The song of the chaffinch has been subjected to a more rigorous analysis than that of the poets by a machine called a sound spectrograph, which records the song on paper as a 'picture' showing the acoustic frequency of the notes at each instant in the song. The chaffinches' song appears as a series of complex 'notes' with the flourish at the end, and recordings of the songs of many individuals show that each one is slightly different, so each can be recognised as a 'signature-tune' by both other chaffinches and humans.

The study of chaffinch song has shown how the birds acquire their song and how chaffinches in one area come to have a similar dialect. Many birds can imitate the songs of other birds or of humans and other animals. Budgerigars and parrots can imitate humans, while several finches, for instance bullfinches and greenfinches, will imitate other birds, but chaffinches pick up sounds only from other chaffinches. In this way a chaffinch sings in the local dialect, because from early in its life it hears the song of its father and neighbouring males. Later, when mature, it learns the fine detail of the song when it has to sing in competition with neighbouring territory-holders.

The song is not completely learnt, however. If chaffinches are reared in isolation from a very early age, they are able to sing, although their song is simpler and quieter than that of a normally-reared bird. This shows that the song is derived from a mixture of learning and instinct. There is a simple, instinctive framework on which the intricacies of the full song are hung as the bird hears and practises them.

class	**Aves**
order	**Passeriformes**
family	**Fringillidae**
genus & species	***Fringilla coelebs***

One of the commonest of all birds, the chaffinch is the commonest of the British finches. It is also found throughout continental Europe, and large flocks migrate yearly to North Africa, Iraq, and the Middle East.

Chaffinch *(Fringilla coelebs)*
winter range   summer breeding range

Top right: *The chaffinches' nest, as befits the delicately mottled eggs which it is built to contain, is one of the most artistic of nests. It is made by the hen working alone, with grass, rootlets and moss, lined with feathers and decorated on the outside with pieces of lichen bound on with cobwebs.*

The male chaffinch, above, *is one of the most beautiful of British birds. Like all the finches he has a stout bill adapted for cracking seeds. Here he is sitting on a dry stone wall on an upland farm but he would be equally at home among the hedgerows and copses of lowland farms or on commons, or in parks and gardens around towns and villages.*

Top left: *A hen chaffinch showing territorial behaviour by attacking its own reflection in a mirror. This is unusual for a female bird.*

Left: *Fledgling chaffinch among flowering oak and gorse. It is ready to leave the nest a fortnight after hatching but cannot fly at first. Its parents lead it into dense cover, still within their territory, where they continue to feed it for a few more days while it becomes more active, flying about and learning to fend for itself.*

André Fatras

Roy Harris & KR Duff

Chalcid wasp

The chalcid wasp is a minute insect belonging to the order Hymenoptera, and is therefore related to the bees, wasps and ants. Some of their closest relations, the so-called 'fairy flies' (family Mymaridae) are the smallest known insects and one species, Alaptus magnanimus, *is 0.12 mm long (about 1/120 in.). Over 1 500 species are known, but their minute size makes them difficult to collect and study, and many more must be awaiting discovery.*

'Big fleas have little fleas . . .'

Big fleas have little fleas upon their backs to bite 'em. And little fleas have lesser fleas, and so ad infinitum.

This old rhyme might well have been written with chalcid wasps in mind for most chalcid wasps are parasites and hyperparasites of other insects. The term 'hyperparasite' means 'parasite of a parasite'. Thus an ichneumon wasp may lay its eggs in a caterpillar and its larvae may in turn be parasitised by a smaller wasp, such as a chalcid. Cases are even known of hyperparasites themselves being parasitised. Many chalcid wasps lay their eggs in the eggs of moths and butterflies, which gives an idea of the minute size of some of them. From one such egg, itself of pin's-head size, 20 or more fully developed and winged chalcid wasps may emerge.

Chalcids are of great economic importance as a means of control of insect pests. One species *Pteromalus puparum* lays its eggs in the newly-formed pupae of white butterflies, destroying great numbers of them. In 1929 the small white butterfly *Pieris rapae*, one of the commonly-known cabbage whites, was accidentally introduced into New Zealand and by 1935-36 was established as a serious pest. In New Zealand it enjoyed the great advantage that the parasites which had controlled its numbers in Europe were absent. As a remedy, some 500 parasitised pupae of the butterfly were sent to New Zealand from England and over 12 000 of the wasps emerged. Most of these were released, and very soon it was found that almost 90% of pupae collected in the wild were parasitised, and the butterfly has, since that time, been well under control.

Another case of pest control by a chalcid wasp is that of the greenhouse whitefly *Trialeurodes vaporariorum* which attacks tomatoes and other glasshouse plants. It can be controlled by fumigation, but this is expensive and may be dangerous. The use of a chalcid wasp *Encarsia formosa* is cheaper and safer for the grower. Tomato leaves bearing parasitised 'scales' (the immature stage of the whitefly) are hung in bunches in the infected glasshouses. After about 3 weeks all the tiny wasps will have emerged and spread through the glasshouse in their search for further whitefly victims, and the pest is soon eliminated. Both the whitefly and the *Encarsia* wasp are species that have been introduced into Britain, probably from the tropics, and will not live in the open in this country.

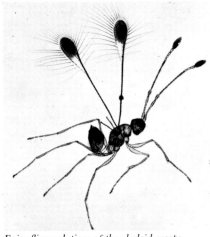

Fairy flies: relatives of the chalcid wasps and among the smallest of known insects. They are so tiny they can parasitise the eggs of other insects.

Not all the chalcids are parasites of insects. Some form galls in plants and others bore in seeds and may be harmful on this account.

Liquid food for adults

Adult chalcids can take only liquid food and probably confine themselves to sucking up water, nectar and honeydew. The food of the larvae depends on their habits; parasitic species feed on the tissues of their host, the others on the tissues and sap of plants.

Wild fig tree. Chalcid wasps breeding in them play a key role in fertilising edible figs.

Young without fertilisation

Many of the chalcids reproduce by parthenogenesis—the females lay eggs which hatch without ever being fertilised. In such species the males are usually rare and sometimes unknown. A more remarkable method of reproduction seen in chalcids is that known as polyembryony. A single egg is laid by the parasite and at an early stage in its development it divides into a number of separate cell masses, each of which develops into a larva. The individuals formed in this way are all of the same sex and genetically identical in every way. They are formed in the same way as human identical twins, but whereas these occur as only a rare developmental accident, identical broods from one egg are normal for many of the chalcids.

Parasitic chalcid wasps usually lay their eggs in the eggs of particular host insects. Some species lay in host eggs in conifer trees, others parasitise the eggs of sawflies and other insects found in galls. Some of the fairy flies enter water and lay their eggs in those of dragonflies and backswimmers or in the larvae of caddis flies. Only one chalcid lays in any one host egg because they can smell the scent of any chalcid that has already been there.

The wasp and the fig

In the Mediterranean region the finest edible fig is the Smyrna fig, but it bears only female flowers and will not form fruit without pollination. The wild fig or 'caprifig', whose fruit is useless, must be grown among the Smyrna fig trees if fruit is to develop, or bunches of caprifigs can be gathered and hung among the branches of the edible fig trees. This was known to the early cultivators of classical times, though they were content to regard the association as mysterious. The explanation is as follows.

Certain chalcid wasps, now known as fig wasps, family Agaontidae, live in galls on the male flowers of wild figs. The male wasps are wingless and can only crawl from one gall to another in search of females, with which they mate. The winged females then search for fig flowers in which to lay their eggs, and in this search they often enter the flowers of the Smyrna figs. They do not lay eggs in them but, having emerged from male wild fig flowers, they carry pollen on their bodies which fertilises the Smyrna fig flowers so that they develop and form fruit. As the wasps can breed in only the wild figs, it is necessary to cultivate these, and to ensure that they are infested by fig wasps, in order to obtain fruit from Smyrna figs. Fig trees are not pollinated by the wind or by any other insects. When fig growing was established in California fig wasps had to be imported from the Mediterranean region.

This does not apply to the common fig which grows in Britain, as this does not require pollination to set fruit.

phylum	**Arthropoda**
class	**Insecta**
order	**Hymenoptera**
family	**Chalcidae**

Chamois

*The chamois is a species of goat-
antelope, goat-like mountain animals
which include the gorals and serows of
Asia. It is sturdy, 4 ft long, 32 in.
at the shoulder and up to 90 lb weight.
The does are smaller than the bucks
and both have horns, up to 10 in. long,
that rise vertically from the head, then
curve back and down to end in sharp
points. The coat is of long hair with a
thick underfur, tawny in summer, dark
brown to black in winter. There is a patch
of white on the throat, some white on the
face and a dark line along the middle of
the back.*

*The chamois is usually thought of as
living on mountain tops, above the
tree line, and going higher up in summer.
In fact, they live mainly in the alpine
forests at about the tree line and only
occasionally go above this. Others will
range as high as the snow line in summer.
At the approach of winter there is a down-
ward movement, some chamois coming
down as far as 2 400 ft. None goes higher
than 4 500 – 6 000 ft, whereas ibex go up
to 7 000 or 8 500 ft.*

*The chamois ranges through southern
Europe into Asia Minor and the Caucasus.
In Europe it is found in the Cantabrian
Mountains, the Pyrenees, Alps, Appenines,
in the Sudeten, Tatra Mountains and the
Carpathians, and in the Balkans. The does
and young live in groups which merge
into herds several hundred strong for the
rut. The bucks are solitary except during
the rut.*

Spring-heel chamois

Apart from their leaping powers, chamois
are noted for their remarkable sight and
hearing, which makes them a difficult
quarry, increasing the skill needed by those
stalking them. A chamois may leap upwards
13 ft, or make a long jump of 23 ft, but even
more outstanding is its ability to move from
one rocky crag to another or to dash across
an almost sheer rock face.

Frank Lane, in his *Nature Parade*, has
described the hooves as being shod with
pliable horn which wears better than the
finest mountain boots, the inner part of each
hoof acting like the welt nails on a climbing
boot. Cup-shaped depressions on the soles
of the hooves give a firm hold on slippery
rocks, and the points of the hooves, the
'aft claws', grip the surface and help to prevent slipping on any but icy slopes. Lane
describes the shock-absorbers in the lower
leg that take the strain of a heavy jump. He
tells of holding the upper part of the leg of
a chamois that had just been shot and
pushing the hoof up and down 'just like a
spring'.

Only broken glass refused

Goat-antelopes are members of the cattle
family, and are intermediate between goats
and antelopes. Chamois seem to have the
digestive powers of a goat. They are

Shy chamois skilfully stalked by a photographer.

grazers and browsers, taking grass and other
sparse mountain herbage, as well as lichens.
They also browse the trees, including the
conifers, with their indigestible pine
needles. No doubt if ever picnic parties
become fashionable at high altitudes the
chamois could be relied upon to clear up
the litter.

Dangerous love-making

The rut begins in mid-October and lasts
until December. The bucks chase each
other, erecting the hair along the mid-line
of the back and bleating with a deep
rumbling note. It is these bristle-like hairs
that form the coveted trophy worn in the
hatband of the successful hunter. The
scent glands on the top of the head, in
both sexes, are then at their peak of activity.
The rivalry between males leads at times to

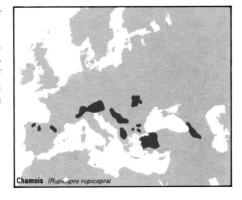

Chamois *(Rupicapra rupicapra)*

one of the adversaries having his belly punc-
tured by the other's horns, resulting in a
fatal peritonitis.

After a gestation period of 153–180 days
1–3 kids are born from mid-May to mid-
June, by which time the herds have once
again split up into small groups. The kids
can follow the doe almost from birth, and
get their early training in mountaineer-
ing by jumping on and off their mothers'
backs. Females mature at about 18 months.
Chamois have lived in zoos for 17 years.

Mountain enemies

Potential enemies are any wolves or lynxes
that penetrate these heights. The greater
danger is to the kids, from foxes and
eagles. Although chamois have long been
hunted the effects have been less disastrous
than with the ibex, largely because so many
remain permanently in the forests.

A disease was noted among chamois in
Switzerland in 1927, and it may be that this is
one of those instances in which an animal
population is kept in check by an endemic
disease, so preventing them from increasing
to such numbers as would damage their
habitat. There is, however, one check on
chamois increases that can be ruled out, if
legend can be believed, and that is death
from falling down a precipice. The legend
accounts for the shape of the chamois'
horns, that they act as shock-absorbers
should the animal fall and land on its head.
This figures in a 12th century bestiary:

'There is an animal called Ibex the
Chamois, which has two horns. And such
is the strength of these, that if it is hurled
down from a high mountain peak to the
very depths, its whole body will be preserved
unhurt by these two.'

Chamois and erosion

In 1901 chamois were imported into New
Zealand to 'induce the world traveller to
include New Zealand in his itinerary and to
tempt our Australian cousins to come across
the Tasman Sea to enjoy the physical mar-
vels and delightful climate of New Zealand.'
The chamois were introduced into South
Island and they flourished along the
Southern Alps. In 1936/37 nearly 3 000 were
shot. Another 1 500 were shot in 1939.
Despite the thousands killed by gunshot and
by an epidemic disease during 1936/40
(similar to that noted in Switzerland) the
chamois are feeding on alpine plants to
such an extent as to cause erosion. Re-
moval of the natural plant cover of the soil
allows it to be washed away by rains. As one
report puts it 'the harmful effects of the
existing populations of these animals out-
weigh their value for sport.' A recent four-
year programme of intensive hunting has
not significantly affected their numbers, and
the problem of soil erosion in New Zealand
due to introduced chamois and deer remains serious.

class	**Mammalia**
order	**Artiodactyla**
family	**Bovidae**
genus & species	***Rupicapra rupicapra***

The cheetah; slim swift
'greyhound' of the cat
family, the fastest
mammal on land

Cheetah

The cheetah is one of the 'big cats', distinguishable from other cats by the way it crouches. The big cats hold their feet out in front of them when crouched, like Landseer's lions in Trafalgar Square, while the small cats tuck their feet in, like a domestic cat. Big cats are more noisy than small cats, some of them being noted for their roaring. The cheetah utters a cry that is described as a 'barking howl'.

The legs of a cheetah are disproportionately long when compared with other cats, and the head is small. The length of head and body is just over 4 ft and that of the tail 2 ft. Cheetahs stand just over 3 ft high and weigh over 100 lb. Altogether, the physique suggests a lithe and speedy creature, and the cheetah is, indeed, the chief claimant to the title of the world's fastest land animal.

The ground colour of the coat is tawny to light grey with white underparts. Most of the body is covered with closely-spaced black spots, merging into black rings on the tail. On each side of the face there is a black stripe running from eye to mouth. In 1927 a second species of cheetah was described from Rhodesia. It was called the king cheetah and had black stripes replacing some of the spots, longitudinal on the back and tail and diagonal on the flanks. The species is based on only a few specimens and may be only a local aberration rather than a true species, or even a recurrent mutant.

Unlike other cats, the cheetah has claws that are blunt and can be only partly retracted.

Diminished range

The range of the cheetah extends from India westwards across to Morocco and Rio de Oro and southwards through the African continent to South Africa, preferring open country. In places, for instance some parts of East Africa, it is still relatively abundant, but elsewhere it is very rare or extinct.

In India it is very unlikely that any survive. EP Gee, the authority on Indian animals, considers, in his book *Wild Life of India*, that they have been extinct for some years. Apart from unconfirmed reports, the last record seems to be of three males being shot in the same place at night using artificial light. This is a sad state of affairs when one considers that the 16th-century Emperor Akbar kept 1 000 cheetahs in captivity for hunting (see Blackbuck, p 224). For some time, scarcity of native cheetahs has forced the Indian potentates to import hunting animals from Africa. The staggering decline of the Indian cheetah was not just due to the trade in coats, rugs and trophies; the spread of agriculture robbed it of its habitat, and its staple food, the blackbuck and axis deer, have been wiped out in many places.

Cheetahs are solitary but sometimes hunt in pairs. Occasionally, small bands of up to a dozen may be seen. These are composed of males and females or males alone. Bands made up of females only have not been seen.

Like other cats, cheetahs have regular scratching posts. This habit is used by trappers who set nooses at the post, with a reasonable certainty of success if the scratch marks are fresh.

Cheetahs can make good, but expensive pets, being affectionate and playful. Many stories in popular magazines attest to their good qualities. However, ownership should be restricted to people experienced in handling animals. An animal weighing a hundred pounds or more, with non-retractile claws, can inflict injury without meaning to do so, and there is always the fear that a cheetah may revert to its normal hunting habits of chasing animals that are moving away from it.

Sprinting hunters

The main prey are small-hoofed animals, chiefly axis deer and blackbuck in India, and Thomson's and Grant's gazelles in Africa. They will also attack large animals such as wildebeeste and zebra, and small animals such as hares probably form a substantial part of the diet. Ostriches and game birds, such as bustards and guinea fowl, are also eaten.

Unlike other cats, who tend to lie in wait for their prey and pounce with a single leap or a short rush when they are close enough, cheetahs will stalk their prey and then race after them, for some distance. In a short sprint they can easily overtake their prey, but if the latter gets a good start, the cheetah will drop out of the chase, exhausted from its burst of violent energy. Having caught up with its prey, the cheetah is said to knock it over and despatch it by seizing its throat and strangling it.

It seems that cheetahs attack only frightened animals. One story tells of four cheetahs trying to frighten a young warthog. The warthog refused to flee and the frustrated cheetahs left it, to kill an impala. If this idea is true, it is good evidence that pet cheetahs should be treated with caution. It would not do to run away from one.

Another story, recounted by a woman who lived in East Africa for some years, illustrates the cheetah's hunting habits. She came across a cheetah sitting within a few hundred yards of some Thomson's gazelles. Having made up its mind to catch one, the cheetah trotted towards them, upwind and making no effort at concealment. The gazelles immediately became alarmed but instead of fleeing they jinked about. Only when the cheetah suddenly bounded towards them did the gazelles break and flee. By this time it was too late, and the cheetah caught its intended victim. The strange part about this story is the careless way in which the cheetah approached its quarry. It certainly suggests that the spotted coat is not employed for camouflage, and it seems strange that the gazelles, which are built for swift running, did not flee immediately.

Captive breeding success

There are few records of breeding in the wild, which appears to take place all the year round. The litter ranges from 2—5 cubs. Observations over a period of years in East Africa suggest that there is a 50% mortality in the first year of life.

It is amazing that the cheetah was the last of the large cats to be bred successfully in captivity. Even today it has been bred in zoos only in a few instances. The first record of successful breeding in captivity was at Krefeld, Germany, in April 1960.

Dr Luciano Spinelli in his private zoo in Rome succeeded in breeding his cheetah 'Beauty'. She gave birth to two litters: one in January, 1966 and one in December, 1966. These two litters were the first recorded cases of cheetahs born in captivity, being successfully reared by their mother. The gestation period was 13 weeks, the cubs weighing $8\frac{1}{2}$—$9\frac{1}{2}$ oz at birth.

At Whipsnade Zoo Park the female cheetah 'Juanita' gave birth to two sets of triplets, one set in September, 1967 and the other in July, 1968.

How fast is the cheetah

The cheetah is traditionally the fastest animal on land, but it is very difficult to find good evidence as to how fast it can run. One difficulty is to know over what distance should the speed be timed. A cheetah is fast over only very short distances. After a few hundred yards it gives up, so although a cheetah will outclass a human athlete in the 200-metres sprint, it is unlikely to complete the course in the 1 500-metres event.

One record that has been widely accepted is for a cheetah running at 71 mph, over 700 yards while timed with a stop-watch. It had also been claimed that it can accelerate to 45 mph in 2 seconds. Later writers have put the maximum speed at 60 mph, but doubt is often cast on this by people who have chased cheetahs with cars. They have suggested speeds of 30—50 mph only, but chasing an animal over, presumably, rough ground while watching a speedometer is not the best way to record speed. At the same time one wonders whether the cheetah is really making an effort to get away, under these circumstances.

The only satisfactory method of settling the dispute about the cheetah's capabilities is to time it over a properly measured course. This has already been tried. In the 1920's cheetah versus greyhound races were staged at Haringey, in London. The results were disappointing, the spectators were more interested in straightforward betting and the cheetah clocked up only 45 mph. But for those who would like to think cheetahs can really run faster, there is the consoling thought that this cheetah was the equivalent of the man who prefers to sit by the fireside on Saturday afternoon. Having failed to catch the hare in the first dash, the cheetah sat down to watch the fun.

class	**Mammalia**
order	**Carnivora**
family	**Felidae**
genus & species	*Acinonyx jubatus*

The long-legged member of the Big Cat tribe

Cheetahs are normally solitary but sometimes hunt in pairs. They qualify as 'big' cats by the way they crouch, with their feet held out in front of them instead of tucked underneath like domestic cats. The cheetah is in a separate genus from the other cats, however, because it has blunt claws that can be only partly retracted. It was once widespread in India but is now probably extinct in that country.

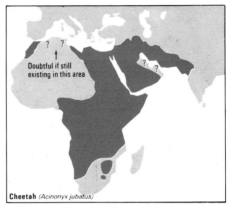

Doubtful if still existing in this area

Cheetah *(Acinonyx jubatus)*

△ *Cheetah slaking its thirst. This and the other picture on this page clearly show the animal's disproportionately long legs; about the same body length as a leopard, it stands a foot higher.*

△ *Cheetah at rest, but still watchful, on the East African plains.*

552

The chickaree is the red squirrel of North America. Despite its engaging habit of sitting up to eat with both hands it is unpopular because it is said to hunt grey squirrels and rob birds' nests of their eggs and young.

A Cruickshank from National Audubon Society

Chickaree

The red, or pine, squirrel of North America is called the chickaree in the west because of its scolding, drawn-out 'churr-churr' call, given when disturbed. About two thirds the size of a grey squirrel, the length of head and body varies from $6\frac{1}{2}-9$ in. with a bushy tail of $3\frac{1}{2}-6\frac{1}{4}$ in. The coat is tawny to brownish, with a rufous band running from the ears to the tip of the tail, and a blackish line along the sides. Around each eye is a narrow ring of white. The tail is fringed with yellow or white hairs and the underparts are white. In winter the colouring is more drab, and the line along the side, which is absent in young animals, disappears. Black or reddish ear-tufts are grown in winter.

There are two species of chickaree: Tamiasciurus hudsonicus ranging from Alaska and Quebec south through the Rocky Mountains to New Mexico and through the Appalachians to South Carolina, and T. douglasii from British Columbia to California. The latter, also known as douglas squirrel, is recognised by a rusty tinge to its underparts.

At home up trees and underground

The main habitat of chickarees is evergreen and deciduous forest, but they are very adaptable, making their homes wherever there is shelter: around houses, in hedgerows, and underground. They dig tunnels or use those abandoned by woodchucks and chipmunks. In the winter, tunnels may be made under snowdrifts. Because they can live underground, or under piles of stones or logs, chickarees have survived the wholesale cutting down of forests that has reduced

the ranges of other tree squirrels.

Nests may be made in the forks of trees, farther out in the foliage, in deserted woodpecker or flicker holes, natural cavities in old trees, and underground, in dry soil, or under stones or stumps. Occasionally an old hawk or crow nest is used as the foundation. The nest is made of three layers. Outside there is a loose maze of twigs with the leaves still attached. Inside this there is a compact, weatherproof layer of compressed leaves, and the inner chamber, 4—6 in. across, is lined with finer material of dried grass, moss, feathers, and fur.

Chickarees are diurnal, but also come out on moonlit nights. They are active throughout the winter, staying in their nests only during very bad weather.

Pine cone diet

Chickarees are wasteful feeders, damaging and rejecting more food than they eat, and storing excessive amounts that will never be eaten. The diet is mainly vegetarian, pine seeds being the staple diet throughout the year. Green cones are cut off the branches in the autumn before they have time to ripen and fall apart. They are carried down the tree and stored in caches of 150 or more in damp soil so they do not ripen before the chickarees need them. Many other seeds, nuts and berries are eaten in due season. In spring the buds of maple and elm are torn up and the chickarees split the bark of maples to suck the syrup. Apples are torn open and the seeds eaten, usually the pulp being left. Fungi are also very popular, and are often stored until dry, lodged in crevices in trees and stumps. Even the deadly fly agaric is eaten, the chickarees apparently being immune to its poisons. At the bottom of the popularity scale are the barks of poplar and aspen, which are eaten in times of famine. As well as vegetable food, insects, such as beetle larvae dug out of timber, carrion and occasionally eggs and young birds are eaten. Sometimes chickarees kill and eat young cottontail rabbits.

▷ *Mating chase of the chickarees by Audubon.*

Douglas' squirrel
(*Tamiasciurus douglasii*)

Chickaree
(*T. hudsonicus*)

Mating chase

Courtship starts in spring sometimes as early as January. As with other squirrels, there is a mating chase in which several chickarees chase each other about the trees and over the ground, each one making a soft, monotonous coughing call. Eventually they pair off and mating takes place in March or April, depending on the climate. Both members of the pair have been reported to help in building the nest, but after that the male takes no part in family life.

The young, 4 or 5 on average, are born after a 40-day gestation. At first they are blind and naked, growing a fine covering of hair by 10 days. They are nursed for 5 weeks, then driven away by their mother who will have a second litter in autumn.

Enemies

Bobcats, mink, the larger hawks and owls will readily take chickarees but their real enemies are the fishers and the closely related American martens which in some parts feed almost wholly on chickarees. They climb almost as well as the squirrels themselves, following them along the thinnest branches and leaping from tree to tree.

Because fur-bearing animals have become rare in many parts, chickarees are sometimes hunted for their pelts, which are used as trimmings.

Anglo-American dispute

It is unfortunate that many animals suffer because folklore has given them an unfair reputation. Rhinoceroses are killed for the supposed aphrodisiac qualities of their horns, and other animals are killed on sight because it is believed that they are harmful to man or his domestic animals. Others suffer from merely a bad name. Squirrels are condemned for being 'tree rats' and water voles for being 'water rats', as these alternatives conjure up pictures of the rightly detested common and ship rats.

The height of such twisted thinking is probably the story of persecution of grey squirrels by red squirrels and vice versa. Squirrels are undoubtedly pests of forestry plantations and are unpopular with the public because they kill baby birds, yet in parts of the United States the chickaree is hunted because it is supposed to hunt and kill the grey squirrel, which is a popular animal. It is even said that chickarees castrate the grey squirrels to prevent them breeding. If enmity does occur it would be surprising if the grey squirrels lost so heavily. They are much larger than the chickarees, and the grey squirrels that have been introduced to Britain are known to kill rabbits, cockerels and even rats and stoats. In fact, there is probably little antagonism

between the two species of squirrel. Studies have shown that they do not often meet and when they do they take little notice of each other.

The story is given an interesting twist, because in Britain it is the grey squirrel that is despised as a cannibal. The introduced grey squirrel is popularly thought to have been responsible for the widespread decrease of the native red squirrel, although its numbers had already sharply declined through disease. Again, both species usually live apart and rarely molest each other.

The reason for the grey squirrel's split role as victim and aggressor probably lies in its position in the sentiments of the public on the two sides of the Atlantic. In Britain it is unpopular, a so-called tree rat, compared with the pretty native red squirrel, whereas in the United States it is held to be decorative compared with the chickaree.

class	**Mammalia**
order	**Rodentia**
family	**Sciuridae**
genus	*Tamiasciurus hudsonicus*
& species	*T. douglasii*

Chicken

*When we say somebody 'keeps chickens'
in his backyard, we mean that the person
owns domesticated fowls of the kind known
scientifically as* Gallus gallus. *This is
also the name of the red jungle fowl of
southern and south east Asia, from the
foothills of the Himalayas to Java. It is
from this the domestic fowl is believed to
have been bred, although some scientists
believe that other wild fowl of the same
region may have been involved, and they
prefer to call the domestic fowl* Gallus
domesticus. *The red jungle fowl lives
in forests from sea level to 5 000 ft.*

*The cock of the wild fowl is mainly red
and black, the black feathers having a
greenish iridescence. The hen is russet
and brown. The cock has a high arched
tail, twin wattles on the throat and a saw-
edge comb. The beak is short and strong,
the legs powerful, the toes on each foot
are armed with strong claws used in
scratching the earth. Of the four toes one
is directed backwards, set at a higher
level than the rest and, in the cock,
armed with a long spur. The wings are
small and rounded, capable of strong
but not sustained flight, consisting of bursts
of wing beats alternating with glides.
Their food is leaves, roots, bulbs, seeds
and berries, earthworms and insects. The
nest is on the ground. The chicks, able to
run about soon after hatching, feed mainly
on insects.*

*The cock's voice is a loud crowing, used
to advertise his possession of a territory.
He is polygamous and defends his territory
if necessary by fighting with beak and spurs.*

Early domestication

The date of domestication of the jungle
fowl is uncertain. It may have been as early
as 3 200 BC but had certainly taken place by
2 000 BC in India. There were domestic
chickens in China by 1 400 BC as well as in
Egypt and Crete, and they reached south-
eastern Europe by 700 BC.

The evidence from archaeological relics,
such as pottery, figurines, coins and mosaics,
suggests that the birds were kept primarily
for religious and sacrificial purposes, as
well as for the sport of cockfighting. They
were later valued for their egg-laying.
According to Aristophanes (about 400 BC)
every Athenian, even the poorest, kept his
hen for laying eggs. The Greeks also in-
vented the capon, or castrated cock, for
fattening, but the eating of chicken flesh
was the least of the economic uses until the
19th century. Another use for the bird was
as an 'alarm clock' for the farmer.

From Ancient Greece to Ancient Rome
was but a short step, and with the Roman
conquest of much of Europe the domestic
chicken was taken farther afield, although it
seems also to have been taken along the
trade routes in advance of the Roman le-
gions. The Celts of northern Europe, for
example, had it before Caesar invaded
Britain.

Hans Gundel

△ *The farmyard's alarm clock; a cock's crow
announces his possession of a territory.*

▽ *An 18th-century cockfight. The sport of cockfighting was one of the earliest uses of chickens.*

Mary Evans

555

Hens in the barnyard

◁ *The chicks can run about soon after hatching, and in the wild would feed mostly on insects.*

▽ *Barnyard family. Cockerels are polygamous and defend their territories, if necessary, by fighting with beak and spurs. There are more than 100 breeds or varieties of chickens, but the number kept for egg or meat production is limited. Modern farming is so specialised that hens are now rarely found scratching around for a living. They tend to be kept in large flocks under standard conditions by poultry farmers only, either in deep litter houses or in batteries of cages. Separate units are maintained with some breeds kept as table birds and others as layers. These mass production units may even be air conditioned with automatic mechanical feeding and watering.*

R Thompson

H Shrempp

Embryology of the chick

Embryology covers the development of a fertilised egg-cell to the emergence of the young animal. The primitive mode of development in vertebrates transforms the whole egg-cell into an embryo, as in the eggs of lampreys and amphibians. Birds' and reptiles' eggs develop in a very different way. Here, of the huge egg-cell (the whole of the yellow yolk) only a small fraction takes part in the formation of the embryo. Development begins when the male's sperm, having swum up the oviduct, unites with a ripe ovum. The ovum at once begins to form a number of cells. It then passes down the oviduct, becoming first coated with albumen and lastly the shell.

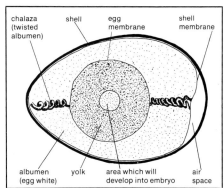

Bird's egg with top half of shell removed
The yolk provides the food so the living cells in the eggs can divide to make the tissues and organs of the young bird. Air can pass through the eggshell and shell membranes.

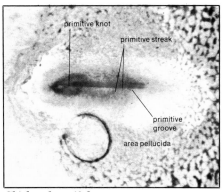

Chick embryo 12 hours
During the first few hours of development cells multiply and move inwards to form a distinct dark area, the primitive streak, which will eventually form the notochord of the chick.

Chick embryo 24 hours
Cells move forward and the head fold is formed. Cells begin to segregate into cube-like body blocks, the somites, on the right and left of the notochord. Six are formed by this stage.

Chick embryo 36 hours
Somite stage, with the brain distinct. The heart, a straight tube, has been formed and blood vessels around the embryo have joined to link with the heart embryo by the vitelline veins.

Chick embryo 48 hours
The brain regions well-differentiated and head turned on left side. Eye parts evident. Heart changed via an S-shape to form chambers. Number of visible somites 27.

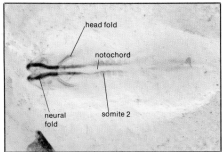

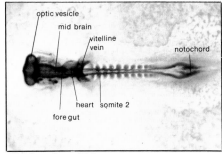

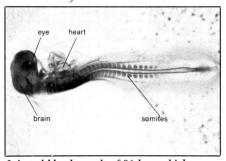

Chick embryo 72 hours
The tail starts to curve. Limb buds beginning to form but hard to distinguish. Olfactory pit visible just above eyes. Increase in size of fore, mid, and hind brain and flexure pronounced.

Chick embryo 96 hours
By 4 days the embryo still looks like almost any young vertebrate. Head and tail curve towards each other. Limb buds well identified but by 6 days show wing and feet characters.

Injected blood vessels of 96-hour chick
A well established network of blood vessels links the embryo with the yolk sac. Blood is carried to and from the yolk sac via the vitelline arteries and veins.

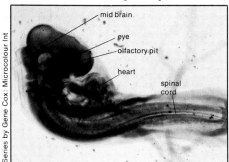

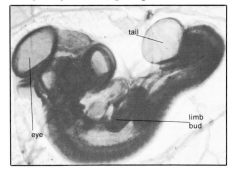

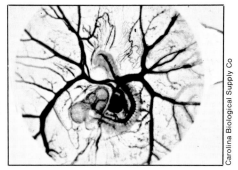

Liberation of life; the chick after about 21 days is fully formed and fractures its eggshell and breaks its way into the world outside.

Series by Gene Cox: Microcolour Int

Carolina Biological Supply Co

Walter Schmidt: Bavaria

Ornamental and commercial breeds

The modern breeds are divided into Mediterranean and Asiatic types. Of the former there are now 37 breeds used commercially, as well as 24 ornamental breeds. In addition to show birds and fighting cockerels, the breeds tend to be grouped into prolific layers and table birds. The names of some are almost household words: the white leghorn, the best egg-layer, closely followed by the Rhode Island red and the Plymouth. Among the ornamental breeds the most spectacular is the long-tailed Yokohama, bred for the long tail, which in the cock may reach 20 ft.

The peck order

In the scientific field chickens have been responsible for one of the biggest advances in our knowledge of animal behaviour. In 1922 the idea of a peck order was first published. It was discovered by observation of the common or farmyard domestic hen. Briefly, it amounts to this: if a dozen hens new to each other are put into an enclosure, they will separate into couples and start to fight. One of each couple will triumph over the other, either because she is stronger than her opponent or because her opponent refuses to fight. She will be dominant, the other will be subordinate.

Then the dominants will face each other in couples, from which half will emerge once more as dominants, the other half as subordinates. In the end a hierarchy will have been established which can be expressed as follows. If we identify the hens by the letters A to L there will be the boss hen (A) which can peck all the others and they will not peck back. The next in succession (B) will be able to peck all except A, C can peck D–L, but not A and B, and so it will go down the line, until the lowest in the hierarchy (L) will be subordinate to all the rest, the one which gets pecked by all the others.

Any hen can change her position in the hierarchy by winning a fight with a superior hen, but without such a challenge the positions in the hierarchy are accepted by all.

This is a simplified version but the principle is there, and subsequent research in a large number of animal species has confirmed it. In most animal communities (including our own) there is a social order of dominance and subordinance, among males as well as females. It is generally referred to as a peck order, because the first discovery was with domestic hens. And the discovery has revolutionized our study of the social behaviour of animals.

Chicken fortune tellers

The behaviour of chickens in their peck order has become almost a symbol in the philosophy of the modern scientist. Chickens have served as symbols in other ways in earlier civilizations. Hens were symbols of fertility, because of their egg-laying, and this was later transferred to the cock, largely from the elaborate display he uses in wooing the hen. He became an erotic symbol as well as a symbol of health.

The Romans went further and used chickens for prophecy, the *oraculum ex tripudio*. Hens were put in a cage with food. If they

△△ *Wild relative — the jungle fowl, which lives in forests from sea level to 5 000 feet. It is characterised by the iridescence of its feathers.*

△ *One of the more exotic breeds: the long-tailed Yokohama. Many varieties have been specially bred for their attractive plumage patterns.*

ate greedily, the omens were good. Should they show little taste for food, the omens were unfavourable. The method was open to abuse. One had only to starve the hens beforehand to obtain a good omen.

In the first Punic War a consul, angry with his hens because they refused to eat when he needed a good omen, cast them into the sea saying: 'Let them drink if they won't eat.' He was subsequently defeated in a battle at sea, a fate which the people of Rome attributed to his lack of respect for the hens.

class	**Aves**
order	**Galliformes**
family	**Phasianidae**
genus & species	***Gallus gallus***

558

...ntent' — relaxed and normal.

F-101-1 © 3M

ana they normally run on all fours, but they can walk upright, with toes turned outwards. When erect they stand 3—5 ft high. The hair is long and coarse, black except for a white patch near the rump. The face, ears, hands and feet are naked and, except for the black face, flesh coloured.

Forest families

The single species of chimpanzee lives in the tropical rain forests of Africa, roughly from the Niger basin to Angola. They are at home in the trees, making nests of branches and vines each night to sleep in, but they often come down to the ground to search for food. Whereas their normal gait on the ground is all fours, they will run on three legs, leaving one free to hold food, or on their hind legs, in an amusing waddling gait, when carrying an armful of food.

Chimpanzees live in small parties, occasionally numbering up to 40, but the bonds between the members of a party are weak. There is no fixed social structure as there is in baboon troops (see p. 268). A chimpanzee party is constantly varying in size as members leave to wander off in the forests by themselves or return from such a wandering. The only constant unit of social life is a mother with her young. She may have two or three of different ages with her at any time because they stay with her for several years. The usual size of a group is from 3—6, but numbers increase as chimpanzees gather at a source of plentiful and tasty food, or if a female comes on heat (that is—becomes sexually attractive) when the males will gather round her for several days.

Within a party, the males are arranged in a social order, the inferior ones respecting the superior ones. Dominance is related to age; a chimpanzee gradually rises in social position from the time he is physically mature and leaves the protection of his mother. The status of a male seems to be partly determined by noisy displays, charging about waving branches or rocks or drumming the feet on the plank-like buttresses of the forest trees. This behaviour is sometimes sparked off by frustration brought on by seeing more dominant males enjoying food without sharing it. Yet the

△ *'Hello' — the greeting pout.*

△ *'I'm happy' smile, showing bottom teeth only.*
▽ *Tantrum, showing top and bottom teeth.*

chimpanzees recognize the right of ownership sufficiently to prevent a dominant male from wresting food from one of his inferiors.

First aid and affection

When chimpanzees meet after having been apart they greet each other in a very human way, by touching each other or even clasping hands and kissing. The arrival of a dominant male is the signal for the rest to hurry over and pay their respects to him. The members of a party also spend a considerable amount of time grooming each other, and themselves. Mothers carefully go through the fur of their babies for any foreign particles, spending more and more time on the task as the babies grow older. Dirt, burrs, dried skin and ticks are plucked off and splinters may be removed by pinching them out with forefingers or lips. Such mutual help may lead to further first aid. A captive female was once seen to approach her male companion, whimpering. She sat down while the other chimpanzee sat opposite her and, holding her head steady with one hand, pulled the lower lid of one eye down with the other. After a short inspection he removed a speck of grit from her eye with his finger, to her evident relief.

Hunting for meat

About 7 hours a day may be spent feeding either up trees or on the ground. The chimpanzees investigate any source likely to produce food. Crevices in logs are searched for insects and nests are robbed of eggs and chicks, but their usual food consists of fruits, leaves and roots. Ripening fruit crops, of bananas, pawpaws or wild figs, are a special attraction to them and they are sometimes a nuisance when they attack plantations. A big male chimpanzee can eat over 50 bananas at one sitting.

Until recently it was thought that the only flesh eaten by chimpanzees was that of insects and occasionally birds and small rodents. They have now been found to hunt larger animals, some individuals apparently being particularly fond of meat. Young bushbucks and bushpigs have been seen caught by chimpanzees, as well as colobus monkeys and young baboons. Jane Goodall, who studied chimpanzees in the wild, has given a very graphic description of a chimpanzee catching a young baboon and killing it by holding its back legs and smashing its head against the ground.

Obedient children

Chimpanzees are promiscuous. When a female comes on heat the males gather round her, bounding and leaping through the branches. All of them mate with her, no matter what their social standing. She remains on heat for several days, then the males lose interest.

A single baby—twins are rare—is born after about 230 days. If it is the female's first baby, she does not at first seem to know what to do with it, but by a combination of instinct, knowledge gained from having seen other babies, and learning, she soon starts to care for it. For 2 years the baby will be completely dependent on her. At first she carries it to her breast, but as it grows larger it rides pick-a-back.

The standard of baby care shown by

Series by Michael Lyster

Top: *Young chimps, Primrose (left) and Peter.*
Right: *Chimpanzees are the best tool-users apart from man, using natural objects to gather food, crack nuts, and drive off enemies.*

Chimpanzee *(Pan troglodytes)*

female chimpanzees varies considerably. Some are ideal mothers, caring for their babies zealously and caressing and kissing them. Others are over attentive, and the babies are 'spoilt'; and yet others neglect their children. The standard of care and education, however, is on the whole exemplary. The babies are not usually bullied or spoiled, yet they obey the parents' orders instantly. When they leave their mother's back they have considerable freedom, and can climb over dominant males without fear.

The babies are carried for varying periods. Sometimes they are still riding on their mothers when 4 years old. By this time the mother will have another baby and the elder one has to fend more for itself, but chimpanzees have been seen hand feeding young that are 6 or 7 years old.

Tools for chimpanzees

Man is sometimes called the toolmaker to distinguish him from other animals. It is difficult to decide when our ancestors became human-like rather than ape-like,

and toolmaking is one factor used as a line of contrast. Upright gait and speech are others, but it is difficult to make rigid pronouncements about features that must have evolved gradually.

Tools can be regarded as extensions of the body used to help with certain tasks. Few animals are known to use tools, but the real difference that separates man and the rest of the animal world is that he not only uses a variety of tools, he makes them, fashioning natural objects to suit his purpose. In this way, opening a nut with a stone is tool using, but shaping the stone into an axe is toolmaking.

Chimpanzees are the best tool-users apart from man. In captivity, they have been seen to throw stones and brandish clubs when put in a cage near a leopard and they are mentally well equipped to work out how to use tools, which are used by some other animals more or less instinctively. Chimpanzees have solved such problems as fitting two sticks together or balancing boxes on top of each other to get at otherwise inaccessible bananas.

The observations by Jane Goodall and others on wild chimpanzees have shown that they also use a variety of tools. The most common use is to extract honey, ants or termites from nests. Sticks 2–3 ft long are picked off the ground or broken from branches and pushed into nests, then withdrawn, and the honey or insects licked off. Stones are used to crack nuts, or as missiles to drive humans or baboons away from the chimpanzees' food. The stones, which sometimes weigh several pounds, are thrown, overarm, not very accurately but definitely aimed. Another material used for tools is leaves. Chimpanzees have been seen plucking leaves, chewing them up, and using the resultant mass as a sponge. Water, in a natural bowl in a tree, was soaked up into the sponge and squeezed out into the chimpanzee's mouth. Whole leaves have also been used for wiping sticky lips and hands after eating bananas.

The variety of tools used by the chimpanzees is made more interesting because they actually make some of their implements. To make a suitable rod to extract insects, the chimpanzees will strip the leaves off a twig or tear shreds off a grass stem to make it narrower. These are clear signs of modifying natural material for a specific use, as is the chewing of leaves to make a sponge. So man is not the only toolmaker, merely better at it than his relatives.

By the late 1980s, chimpanzees have become extinct in four African countries and severely endangered in 11 others. Young chimpanzees are taken illegally from their African rain forest for sale in foreign markets, where private zoos still provide demand. (They are also used in animal experiments.) Continuing destruction of their native forests is contributing to their worsening plight.

class	**Mammalia**
order	**Primates**
family	**Pongidae**
genus & species	***Pan troglodytes***

Chimpanzee first-aid: incredible instance of male removing grit from his mate's eye.

A mother suckles her baby. Chimpanzees show great affection to their young, and discipline is good without the need for bullying.

Chinchilla

Best known for its remarkably soft fur, which is 1–1½ in. long, the chinchilla is a rodent related to viscachas, agoutis (see p. 61) and guinea pigs. It resembles a small rabbit, is 10 in. long, and has a squirrel-like tail. The ears are almost naked, the whiskers very long and the eyes large. The small feet have weak claws on each of the four toes. The soles of the feet are rubbery. The colour of the fur is a bluish-grey with faint dusky markings.

Chinchillas should not be confused with chinchilla rats Abrocoma, *chinchilla mice* Chinchillula *or* Euneomys, *and chinchilla rabbits, a fancy variety of rabbit, so called because of its soft, chinchilla-like fur.*

A mountain home

Chinchillas once thrived in the Andes in Peru, Bolivia, Chile and Argentina, from sea-level to 20 000 ft. They have been hunted so much for their fur that wild chinchillas now survive in only the northern regions of Chile, high in the mountains. They live a communal life in burrows or among rocks in the semi-arid mountain areas. They are nocturnal, but will bask in the morning and evening sun. Before their numbers were depleted, as many as 100 could be seen together.

Despite the number killed, very few specimens of chinchillas found their way into museum collections and the exact number of species has been debated. Recently it was thought that there were two species: one, with a long tail and ears, living at low levels, while the other, with a short tail and ears, lived up the mountains. It is now thought these may be variations due to climate, however, and not truly specific differences. There is a marked tendency towards the lessening of extremities in cold climates. Mice reared at, say, 20°C/68°F have shorter tails than those from the same stock reared at higher temperatures, say 30°C/86°F. As, therefore, chinchillas living at 15 000 ft have smaller ears and shorter tails than those living at 5 000 ft, it is most likely that they do not represent different species, but are just races of a single species.

Dabbling in the dew

On the slopes of the Andes the only food available for the chinchillas is hardy, coarse grasses and herbs, which are held in the forepaws and eaten while sitting back on the haunches. There is little water in these areas and the chinchillas rely on water obtained from the plants and from dew.

Breeding in a cold climate

Chinchillas mate for life, and the female is the dominant member of the pair. She is slightly larger than the male, and if there is any fighting, she wins. Courtship begins with the male or the female pulling tufts of fur from the other's body. A litter consists usually of 5 or 6 young. The long gestation offers some advantage in this bleak habitat. The gestation time for chinchillas living at 8 000 ft is 115 days, and 125 days for those living at 20 000 ft. The parent weighs less than a rabbit, yet retains its young four times as long. The young chinchillas enter the world having already passed the most helpless stages of infancy, arriving fully furred and not so liable to lose heat. They can run about in a few hours, but, for greater protection against the cold weather of the mountains, they nestle between the two parents who squat side by side to form a furry nest.

The young begin to eat solid food in a week, but are not weaned until 7 or 8 weeks old. They become sexually mature in less than a year. Mating takes place a few minutes to a few days after a female has given birth to a litter, and 1–3 litters may be born each year.

Extinction prevented

Before Europeans reached South America, chinchillas were providing the Indians with warm clothes. The rich wore robes made of whole skins, while the poor wove blankets from thread made of hair clipped from the chinchillas. The introduction of chinchilla fur to Europe is said to have happened when a Spanish captain obtained a chinchilla robe from an old chieftain to keep himself warm during the cold nights. The captain's mission was to collect tribute in the form of jewels and gold, and in this he was not too successful. So in case he should be imprisoned for dereliction of duty he decided to cut his losses, hide the valuables and send his chinchilla robe to Queen Isabella. Luckily for him, she reacted as many women have since reacted to chinchilla fur and forgave the captain, saying that the robe was a better gift than gold and jewels.

Despite this successful start, chinchilla fur did not become popular until the 18th century and only in the 19th did its use become exorbitant, the peak coming in 1899 when half a million pelts were exported from Chile alone. Not surprisingly, chinchillas became rare and in the 1900's the South American governments put a tariff on their export. This led to smuggling, and a few years later a ban was put on hunting and exporting chinchillas. There were so few left, however, that it was hardly worth hunting them. Government farms were then set up in the 1920's and the continued, if precarious, existence of the chinchilla was assured.

The next stage was the establishment of chinchilla farms outside South America, which became so flourishing that prices dropped, not catastrophically, but sufficiently to protect the wild stock by making hunting uneconomical. The first chinchillas to leave South America were 11 brought home by an animal-loving American engineer. He had caught 17 but he could obtain an export permit for only 11, and to complicate matters further, he was forbidden to keep them in his stateroom. So he smuggled them aboard and hid them until the ship sailed. They had to be kept in his stateroom because the engineer thought that they would suffer from the heat as the ship crossed the tropics, and constant attention with ice-cubes was needed. This treatment was successful and 11 chinchillas reached California; one had died and one had been born. During the next 3 years they became acclimatised and an artificial diet was perfected. They then began to breed, eventually making the engineer's son a millionaire.

class	**Mammalia**
order	**Rodentia**
family	**Chinchillidae**
genus & species	***Chinchilla laniger***

▷ *Enjoying a quiet roll in the sand (probably important in the grooming of its long fur) a chinchilla reveals its long back legs which resemble those of rabbits and hares. But the chinchilla has only 3 or 4 toes, and also has a long and bushy tail. Another difference is that, although the parent chinchilla weighs less than a rabbit, it retains its young before birth four times as long. To cope with the cold of the Andes mountains, chinchillas are born fully furred. The richness of its fur (below) nearly led to the animal's annihilation by fur hunters.*

Jane Burton: Photo Res

◁ *A young Chinese water deer, a natural denizen of Far Eastern river valleys. It will thrive without access to water in captivity, and is equally at home on English estates—such as the Duke of Bedford's Woburn Park.*

Chinese water deer

A very small deer of China and Korea which is better known in captivity than in the wild, the Chinese water deer stands 17½−21½ in. at the shoulder and is about 3 ft long. Its weight is 20−24 lb. Its tail is a hairy stump. The coat is a light yellowish-brown to pale reddish-brown in summer, turning to dark brown in winter. The underparts and a narrow perpendicular band on the muzzle are white. There is little difference between the sexes. The males do not have antlers, but their upper canines are long and tusk-like, their points reaching well below the lower jaw. Another peculiarity is a small scent gland in the groin on either side, a position unique among deer.

It has been suggested that the water deer and muntjac, which is similar in size, tusks and habitat, are close to the ancestral deer which had tusks and no antlers. In the muntjac the tusks are smaller than in the water deer, and it has small antlers.

It is therefore assumed that the water deer is nearer the ancestral deer, and that in the family of true deer as the antlers developed so the need for tusks grew less until, in the more advanced types, like the roe deer, only antlers remained.

Unique deer families

The Chinese water deer is unique among deer in giving birth to up to 7 fawns, although 4−5 is usual and the doe has only 4 teats. Even this is 2 more than in other deer. The breeding season is in autumn and early winter, when there is much fighting between bucks. They deliver slashing cuts with their tusk-like canines inflicting serious wounds, which are, however, seldom fatal. In captivity they have lived up to 11 years. The young are born in May−June.

Rabbit-like deer

One part of the water deer's range is the marshy beds in river valleys in the basin of the Yangtze River, especially among the tall reed beds fringing its banks and in long grass, but it has also been reported from mountainsides and farmlands. In captivity it thrives without access to water, although it will enter pools or ponds if available. A darker race of this water deer lives in Korea.

The habitat is variable, but the deer seems to prefer long grass into which it scuttles, like a rabbit, at first alarm, or it may run for a distance, bounding rabbit-like before dropping flat in grass. The water deer lives in small groups, which evidently are closely-knit socially. In captivity, when one is removed from the group for a while, the others refuse to accept it on its return.

Their food is mainly grass but, judging by their tastes shown in captivity, this is probably supplemented by other plants.

Animal colonists

The Chinese water deer was first made known to western scientists in 1870, and in 1873 a living specimen was received at the London Zoo. Others followed in succeeding years and, in 1929-31, 32 were taken to Whipsnade and to Woburn Park, belonging to the Duke of Bedford, and kept in semi-captivity, where they thrived. During the early 1940's some escaped from both places and began to spread into neighbouring counties. In 1944 a few of the deer were sent from Woburn to private parks in Hampshire, in the south of England, and in 1950 and 1954 more were sent north to Yorkshire. From all these, some deer escaped but it is in southern England especially that they have become established as feral deer. It is not easy to say how much or how far they have spread, or in what numbers they are now free in the countryside, but every now and then one hears reports of a deer that bounds like a rabbit in places where the water deer was not previously known. They are adept at keeping out of sight, and consequently their presence is not always detected.

In 1901 and again in 1946 a few water deer were sent from Woburn to the New York Zoological Park and their behaviour there sheds light on the ease with which they can break out of captivity. It was found, for example, that fences of 4 in.×6 in. mesh offer no obstacles to the young deer, and a much smaller mesh is needed to prevent their escape.

As is usual with small deer, like the muntjac of Asia and the chevrotains of West Africa, local beliefs arise from the ease with which they can escape observation. It is said that they were left unmolested in China because of local superstition, and in Korea their bite is said to be fatal. People who keep water deer in parks in England testify to the need for avoiding the slashing thrusts of their canines, and this alone could quickly breed respect if not superstition about the danger from them.

class	**Mammalia**
order	**Artiodactyla**
family	**Cervidae**
genus & species	***Hydropotes inermis***

▷ Top: *On the alert. Shy and hard to spot, the water deer has been responsible for the rise, in its native land, of several superstitions based on its skill at remaining unseen. Centre: At the least alarm these 18-inch high miniatures will vanish into long grass with a rabbit-like scuttle. Bottom: Slashing wounds often result from the tusks of the water deer buck in fights during the mating season. These tusks may be a link with ancestral deer, before antlers replaced tusks.*

△ *Chipmunks feed mainly on berries, fruit, nuts and seeds—but they never store any fruit or flesh likely to go bad.*

Chipmunk

There are 2 genera of chipmunks among many kinds of ground squirrels. The eastern chipmunk is the larger of the two, with head and body measuring 5—7 in. and the tail 3—9 in. The fur is reddish-brown with dark stripes on the back, alternating with two lighter stripes. The tail is not as bushy as that of tree squirrels. The western or Siberian chipmunk has a smaller body than the eastern chipmunk, being about 4 in. long, but the tail is as long. Its fur is lighter and there are 5 lightish stripes between the dark ones. The two genera are readily distinguished by the rufous rump of the eastern chipmunk and by the teeth. The eastern chipmunk has one upper premolar (grinding tooth) on each side of the jaw, and the Siberian chipmunk —a north Asiatic ground squirrel and a proficient climber—has two.

The names eastern and western chipmunks refer to their distribution in North America. The single species of eastern chipmunk lives in most of the eastern United States and south eastern Canada, where it thrives in regions of deciduous forest and shrub, being found around fallen logs, rocks or outbuildings. The western chipmunks, of which there are about 17 species, live in North America from the Yukon to Sonora in Mexico, and are spread across Asia from northern Russia through Siberia to northern China and northern Japan. There are 16 American species and one, the Siberian chipmunk, extends across Asia. They are widely distributed within their ranges, except in dense forests. On the whole, the western chipmunks prefer more open country, and are abundant in pasture land and on rocky cliffs.

Permanent residents

Chipmunks are active by day and are good climbers, but prefer to stay on the ground, although the eastern chipmunks sometimes rear their young in trees. They make a complicated system of burrows underground, often running under logs and stones, or delving several feet under the turf. Each burrow is owned by one chipmunk who continues digging throughout its life, so that the burrows may reach lengths of 30 ft or more, and have more than one entrance and perhaps several side chambers, one of which probably contains a nest of leaves and grass.

Although common animals, chipmunks rarely become pests of agriculture or forestry, and when they do they can be controlled easily. Apart from this damage, they are popular animals and readily become tame, visiting campsites to steal food or to accept it from the hand.

Chipmunks do not hibernate in the strict sense, but during bad weather they go into a state of torpor, awakening every now and then to feed from their caches of supplies.

Wide variety of food

The main food is berries, fruits, nuts, and small seeds, which are collected after they have fallen to the ground, or harvested by climbing trees and shrubs to pick them. Fungi, grass and leaves are also eaten. The chipmunks are also carnivorous, taking slugs, snails, aphids and other insects. Small birds, eggs, mice and small snakes are also taken, and in the Sierra Nevada the eastern chipmunk is considered one of the chief enemies of the rosy finch.

Food that is not immediately needed is carried in the cheek pouches and cached for use in the winter. The cheek pouches are loose folds of skin, naked inside but not moist, that open into the side of the mouth. To fill its pouches, a chipmunk holds a nut in its paws, neatly bites off the sharp point on each end and slips it into one pouch. The next nut is placed on the other side and the pouches are filled alternately so that the chipmunk's face, although looking extremely bizarre, is at least balanced. It can take up to four nuts in each pouch and another between the teeth.

Breeding in burrows

Mating takes place from February to April, the males seeking out the females in their burrows. The young are born 31 days later. The babies, 2−8 in number, spend a month in the nest then begin to accompany their mother on foraging trips above ground, venturing further each time. They stay together for 6 weeks then go off on their own. There may be two litters in one year.

Not so safe in burrows

Coyotes, bobcats, foxes, hawks and owls prey on chipmunks. Weasels and snakes are their worst enemies as they can follow them into their burrows, where they are safe from other predators. When danger threatens, the chipmunks alert each other with an alarm call, and dash to cover. The alarm call is a guttural scolding or a whistle.

Misers' hoards

To compare someone with a squirrel is to condemn him as an inveterate hoarder who fills his house with all manner of objects, not so much with any end in mind, but because something might come in useful sometime, and it would be a pity to get rid of it. Chipmunks are probably the most expert hoarders of all the squirrel family but, unlike their human namesakes, they are selective about the things they hoard. When a chipmunk is collecting its winter store, it selects only nuts and cones, never any fruit or flesh that would go bad. The chipmunk takes first prize, however, for the sheer bulk of its stores. Reports have been made of caches containing '8 quarts of acorns' or 'a bushel (32 quarts) of nuts', and one cache does not form a chipmunk's complete winter store. More than one cache may be made in the burrow, and small caches are made all over the chipmunk's home range. In this way it combines the behaviour of the chickaree that makes one or two large stores, and the grey squirrel that makes many small ones. Like the grey squirrel, the chipmunk forgets the position of its small, scattered stores which consist of just a mouthful of nuts buried under leaves or turf. During the winter it may find some of them by smell, otherwise they remain hidden until they germinate and contribute to the growth of the woodland. So the chipmunk does not have to venture into bad weather to feed and, to save further trouble, the store is usually placed in the legendary hideaway of human misers—under the bed!

class	**Mammalia**
order	**Rodentia**
family	**Sciuridae**
genera & species	***Tamias striatus*** *eastern chipmunk* ***Eutamias sibiricus*** *Siberian chipmunk* *others*

▽ *One for the road; a chipmunk can hold about four nuts in each cheek pouch with another in its teeth. A chipmunk's winter store is made up of many caches; there are reports of hoards of up to 32 quarts of nuts.*

Chough

The name chough covers two species belonging to the crow family, each a little larger than a jackdaw. The common or Cornish chough has a glossy blue-black plumage, sometimes with a greenish tinge on wings and tail, as in the magpie. It is readily recognizable by a long, curved red bill and red legs, although the bill of the juveniles is yellowish-red. The alpine chough is very similar but has a shorter, yellowish bill and a very different call, a most un-crowlike shrill, rippling cry. The call of the Cornish chough resembles a jackdaw's 'caw', but is higher and more musical. The old pronunciation of the name, 'chow', is an imitation of the chough's call.

The Australian white-winged chough Corcorax melanorhampus *is one of a crow-like family. It is a resident of eastern Australia and looks like a large jackdaw, with a curved bill like the true choughs, showing white on its primary wing feathers when the wings are spread.*

Marianne Leib: Bavaria

Disappearing cliff-dwellers
The Cornish and alpine choughs are both widespread over Europe and southern Asia, the Cornish chough preferring sea cliffs and the alpine chough preferring inland mountain precipices, but their distribution overlaps considerably. The Cornish chough is generally more numerous, but the alpine chough is found at higher altitudes. In Europe, the Cornish chough is found on the western coasts of Britain, as far west as the Blaskets off Ireland, in Brittany, most of Spain, parts of the Alps, southern Italy, Sardinia and Sicily, Greece and parts of the Balkans. An isolated colony in Ethiopia, 1500 miles from any other, is probably a relict from an ice age when the whole population would have moved south. The alpine chough is found in many parts of the Alps, northern Italy, Corsica, the Balkans and Greece, and Spain except for the south-western corner. Both species live in parts of the Middle East and extend across southern Asia to China.

In Britain the numbers of Cornish choughs have decreased over the last two centuries. They once bred in many parts of England, but later became restricted to Cornwall. Even there they have not bred since 1952 and now none are left. However, they seem to be holding their own in Wales and Ireland. In Scotland they once bred inland but are now confined to the islands of Islay, Jura and others in the southwest of the country. In all, the total population in the British Isles was some 700 pairs in 1963, the last time a count was made.

The decline in Britain has been paralleled over the rest of Europe, and there is no ready explanation for this. Except for the raven, the crow family has tended to flourish, despite man's activities. One explanation is that the choughs are unsuccessfully competing against the jackdaw, which is increasing. This is apparently the case in Spain and there are records of both chough and jackdaw competing for nest places. If the disappearance of the chough is due to competition with another species, it is worth drawing attention to the fact that man is not the only cause for reduction or extinction of a species. Even without him, the balance of nature is continually shifting with the resulting extinction of some species.

Choughs are regularly found at high altitudes. In the Himalayas they have been found breeding up to 19000 ft, and breed regularly at 17000 ft. On one occasion, a Mount Everest expedition found choughs at 27000 ft. Survival in such thin air must present problems since birds need much oxygen for flight, and flight, itself, must be difficult in rarefied air.

Scavenging feeders
Choughs feed largely on insects and their larvae which they get by thrusting their bills into the soil. In this way they take caterpillars, wireworms, ground beetles and ants. Insects and other invertebrates are also caught from among stones and rocks, and some plant material is also eaten. Often flocks of choughs can be seen quartering the ground in long, bounding hops, in the manner of rooks, with whom they will associate, together with jackdaws and crows. The alpine choughs, especially, scavenge rubbish dumps for anything edible, and often they become quite tame.

Lizards and, perhaps, rodents are sometimes eaten, and sheep are said to be attacked during the lambing season.

Nesting in the Great Wall of China

The nests are untidy constructions of twigs, heather, bracken and other material, often including sheep's wool. The favourite sites are on high ledges on cliff walls, or in the roofs of sea caves. Inland, abandoned buildings, mountain ledges and quarries are used, buildings being more often used by the Cornish chough in Asia, where it nests in the Great Wall of China, for instance. In many places choughs nest in colonies.

The clutch is 3 or 4, up to 7. The 17- or 18-day incubation begins when the first egg is laid, so the chicks hatch out at intervals. All the incubation is done by the female, who is fed during this time by her mate. The young stay in the nest for 40 days, and are fed by the parents who together go out foraging. After the chicks have been fed, the male parent feeds the female. The young birds spend a few days wandering around the cliff near the nest, then begin to fly and are taken out on foraging trips by the parents, where they learn to find their own food.

Just for the fun of it

Whether animals enjoy themselves and do things for pleasure is often hotly debated. People who keep animals as pets often assert that they do things with obvious enjoyment, whereas some scientists who keep animals in small cages will say that their behaviour is mechanical and enjoyment or appreciation of what they are doing is impossible.

Choughs certainly behave as if they are enjoying themselves. One of the most notable features of their behaviour is their habit of playing in the air currents around cliff faces. Finding an updraught, they will shoot upward with head and body vertical, then flip over and plummet down with wings folded, levelling out just before hitting the sea. At other times they turn somersaults in the air. It is impossible to think of any benefit that the choughs could get from this behaviour.

The choughs' distant relatives, the Australian choughs, also seem to enjoy their play. One of their games is 'follow the leader'. One bird walks quickly away from the flock and the others chase it over the ground and up and down trees. At other times one will pick up a stick and the others will try to wrest it away. If that is not play, what is it?

class	**Aves**
order	**Passeriformes**
family	**Corvidae**
genus & species	***Pyrrhocorax pyrrhocorax*** *Cornish chough* ***P. graculus*** *alpine chough*

Far left: *Choughs in the Alps. Climbers even on the upper slopes of Everest have found their camps visited by choughs.* Top: *A colony of choughs wheels in the air currents above a ruined tower. Abandoned buildings and ruins are favourite nesting sites for choughs.*

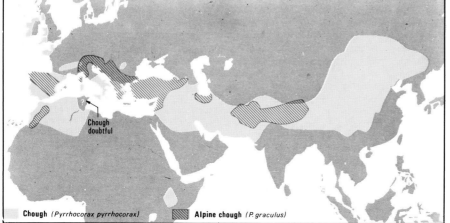

Chough doubtful

Chough (*Pyrrhocorax pyrrhocorax*)   Alpine chough (*P. graculus*)

A Niestlé: Bavaria

569

From a distance the chuckwalla is a dull dark-skinned lizard. A close-up, however, shows the beautifully detailed patterns and colours of its scales.

Chuckwalla

The chuckwalla is a plump lizard, usually 10 – 12 in. long, but it may attain 18 in. It weighs 3 – 4 lb when mature. The colour is variable, being shiny just after the annual moult, the general impression being of brown or black. Along the back run lines of dark brown which continue down the tail. As the males grow older, the brown lines disappear as the body becomes generally lighter. The tail becomes almost white. These differences help to identify the sex of a chuckwalla, but must be used with caution because the young males and females are so alike, and because the largest females also resemble males.

A desert habitat

The chuckwalla lives in desert regions, in areas of rock and lava in western parts of the United States, from Utah and Arizona southwards, and the northern borders of Mexico. Each chuckwalla keeps within a home range but they do not have regular 'homes' or retreats. When resting or in times of danger, they retire to any rock crevice available. The ranges of male chuckwallas never overlap, boundary threat displays no doubt keeping them apart, but one or more female ranges may well overlap that of a male, a fact which presumably helps bring the sexes together in the breeding season. A study of the chuckwallas' ranges showed that the males' ranges are three times as big as the females', which cover about half an acre.

In their hot desert homes chuckwallas are active for only part of the year, from late March to early August, when there is most food. Later in the year temperatures rise, the humidity drops through the lack of rain and plants become dormant or wither up.

Faced with a shortage of food and water the chuckwallas disappear below ground and aestivate, not emerging even when conditions are temporarily favourable. The aestivation, or summer sleep, becomes hibernation, or winter sleep, as the vegetation remains parched all winter.

Chuckwallas are active during the day, coming out in air temperatures of $20° – 40°C/68° – 104°F$. They are most active in the morning before the sun becomes too hot, and during the morning they spend some time basking. They are able to control their body temperature to some extent while basking. When the sun becomes too hot, they move to the shade or lie so that less of the body is exposed to the sun. The body colour also becomes lighter, so some of the sun's rays are reflected instead of being absorbed.

Flower-eating lizard

The most usual diet for lizards is small animals, especially insects, but chuckwallas have been seen to eat flesh only in captivity, when they eat mealworms and mice. In the wild, as far as we know, they eat plants, favouring blossoms, such as those of the prickly pear and creosote bushes, rather than leaves, fruit or shoots.

When the chuckwalla emerges in the morning it basks for a while until its body has warmed up and it can become active. It then forages around its home range, wandering from plant to plant nibbling at the flowers, and sometimes the leaves. Chuckwallas seem to prefer yellow flowers. As well as browsing on annuals and ground-hugging shrubs, they also climb up the higher shrubs, clambering around the outside to get at the flowers rather than climbing through the inner branches.

Multiple mating

Breeding takes place in the spring and early summer so that the young chuckwallas will have a plentiful supply of food.

Courtship has not been observed, but the peak of mating probably occurs in May. As female ranges overlap the males' ranges it is probable that one male may mate with several females, and, more important, one female mate with several males, for this will increase the chances of fertilisation of the eggs. Males are fertile every year, but it appears that females produce eggs only one year in two. This could be because it is difficult to build up the necessary body reserves for forming the eggs in such an arid habitat, and flowers are not very nutritious.

An American zoologist once found a chuckwalla laying her eggs, but he was unable to ascertain how many were laid or how long they took to hatch because the nest was later raided by an unknown predator, although in San Diego Zoo another chuckwalla laid a clutch of 10 eggs. However, the zoologist was able to watch the process of nesting. The female chuckwalla dug a 4in. wide hole horizontally into a bank of sand, to a distance of 15 in. As she dug in, the entrance became blocked with sand that she was pushing back. After laying the eggs, she turned and scraped this sand back in to cover the clutch.

Chuckwallas saved by a tight squeeze

Chuckwallas are vulnerable to predators when they are feeding, especially if surprised when climbing up bushes. Little is known of their actual predators, but they no doubt fall prey to various hawks and carnivores.

On being surprised, a chuckwalla rushes to the nearest rock crevice, where it wedges itself in by its toes. It is difficult to dislodge because, when pulled backwards the body scales catch on the rock. The tail is folded back out of the way, but if the lizard is touched it lashes out. Perhaps this deters the enemy, or is offered as a sacrifice, the enemy taking the tail and leaving the rest of the lizard. To increase its hold in the crevice it blows its body up with air. A fully inflated chuckwalla increases its body volume by over half and so can exert a considerable force against the walls of its hideout. The Red Indians used to consider chuckwallas a great delicacy, and to extract them from their hideouts they would stab them with a sharp stick, deflating the lungs.

class	**Reptilia**
order	**Squamata**
suborder	**Sauria**
family	**Iguanidae**
genus & species	***Sauromalus obesus***

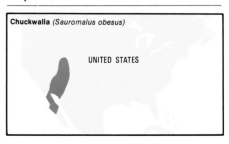

Chuckwalla *(Sauromalus obesus)*

UNITED STATES

Cicada

Some cicadas are among the biggest of all insects and most are fairly large. The Malaysian empress cicada Pomponia imperatoria *has a wingspan of 8 in. Apart from their size and impressive appearance cicadas are remarkable for their extraordinarily loud 'voices', and for the very long period spent in development by some species.*

The family Cicadidae, included in the suborder Homoptera of the order Hemiptera, is related to the aphids, frog-hoppers and scale-insects. Cicadas have a rather broad, flattened body and two pairs of large wings with a characteristic pattern of veins. The longitudinal veins do not extend to the edge of the wing but stop short of it, leaving a narrow, uninterrupted margin along the outer border of each wing. The wings are usually transparent but in some species they are coloured and patterned, the wing membrane being pigmented, so the colour cannot be brushed off as it can in butterflies and moths, whose wings are covered with loosely attached scales.

Cicadas are mainly tropical, extending into the temperate regions in small numbers. A few species occur in southern Europe and about 75 in North America. One, Cicadetta montana, *is found, very rarely, in the New Forest in Hampshire, but is not known from any other British locality. More than 1 500 species are known throughout the world.*

Singing insects

Adult cicadas spend much of their time sitting rather high up on the trunks of trees or among the branches and foliage, singing intermittently. Some species sing during the day, others only at dusk or dawn. When approached they fly off suddenly and are difficult to catch. Their flight is fast and powerful and many of them, like moths, are active at night and fly to artificial lights.

A species found in the Amazon forests *Hemisciera maculipennis* has the basal part of both wings coloured, the forewing opaque olive green, the hindwing vivid vermilion. When the insect is at rest the forewing overlies the hindwing and only the inconspicuous dark green patch is visible, but on taking flight the cicada displays a sudden flash of bright red. This is an instance of 'flash coloration', an adaptive device which probably serves to startle and confuse a predator which finds the insect at rest.

Artificial rain

Like all members of the order Hemiptera, cicadas have mouthparts adapted for piercing and sucking, and they feed on the sap of plant stems and succulent shoots. Most of this sap is sugar and water, so the cicadas must suck up large quantities to make an adequate meal. The result is that large amounts of a weak sugary solution are rapidly excreted. If it appears to be raining under a tree in a tropical forest when the

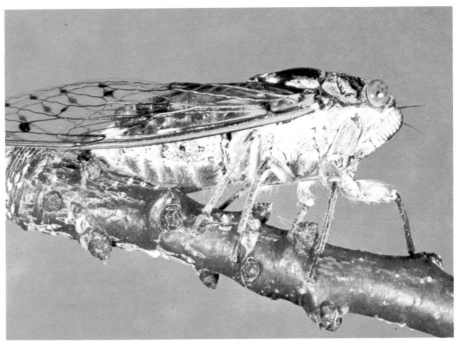

GS Giacomelli

△ *Adult cicada photographed from below to show its sound-box cover just behind the third leg.*

▽ *Adult cicada emerging from the skin of its nymph phase which feeds underground.*

Carolina Biological Supply Co

sky is clear cicadas are probably feeding overhead, and the 'rain' consists of drops of sugary water excreted by them.

The wingless young insects or nymphs, living underground, extract sap from roots in the same way.

17-year locust

The eggs are laid in slits in the twigs of trees and the nymphs fall to the ground after hatching several weeks later. They dig down with their broad, powerful front legs and quickly disappear underground.

After a variable period of feeding, the nymph digs its way to the surface and climbs up a tree. There it rests. Its skin splits, and the adult winged insect emerges. In some species the nymph builds an earthen cone or chimney projecting several inches above the ground, in which it remains for a time before its final transformation.

In the North American species *Magicicada septendecim* the nymph spends no less than 17 years underground in the course of its development. It is known as the 17-year locust. This does not mean that they appear

in a district only once in 17 years, as there may be several broods in different stages of development. The cicadas, do however, appear at irregular intervals of several years, usually recurring in a 17-year cycle. The breeding period has also been checked by observation of nymphs in captivity. There was a major occurence of adult 17 year "locusts" in 1987.

Birds are main predators
Cicadas are extensively preyed on by birds, which give a warm welcome to the great swarms of periodical cicadas that appear in North America. In that country they are also hunted by a large solitary wasp called the cicada killer *Sphecius speciosus* which stocks its nest with paralysed adult cicadas as a provision of food for its own larvae.

The loudest insect voice
The best known insect vocalists are the grasshoppers and crickets, which produce sound by stridulating – the quick stroking of a ridge over a roughened edge or surface. Cicadas sing by a quite different and much more efficient method, if it is judged by the sheer volume of sound. Some cicadas can be heard a ¼ mile away and, close to, they can make ordinary conversation impossible.

In almost all cicadas it is only the males that sing, but both sexes are vocal in a few species. Both sexes always have hearing organs and can, of course, recognise the song of their own species.

The purpose of the song seems to be to call the local population of any one species together so that it forms a small group in which males and females can meet readily.

The singing apparatus consists of a pair of membranes at the base of the abdomen, each surrounded and held by a stiffly elastic ring. The membrane is convex when relaxed, but a muscle attached to it can pull it down and allow it to pop back, rather as a distorted tin lid can be popped in and out. In cicadas the membranes, or *tymbals* as they are called, oscillate at a rate from over 100 to nearly 500 times a second. Other muscles, attached to the ring, distort its shape, affecting the volume and quality of the sound, and the whole apparatus is enclosed in a pair of resonating chambers which amplify the sound and vary it by opening and closing.

By means of this extraordinary musical instrument the cicada can not only make a deafening noise, but each species can produce a sort of 'signature tune' of its own. A good tropical entomologist knows the songs of his cicadas just as a birdwatcher recognizes the calls of birds.

◁ *Mating cicadas.*

phylum	**Arthropoda**
class	**Insecta**
order	**Hemiptera**
suborder	**Homoptera**
family	**Cicadidae**

The insistent song of the cicada
1. Cicada underside: sound-boxes are covered by a protective plate or operculum.
2. The cicada's muscular attachment, showing the tymbal's position in the air cavity which helps amplify the sound. 3. A cross-section through the thorax shows the powerful muscles attached to the tymbal sound-boxes, which have concave inner surfaces.

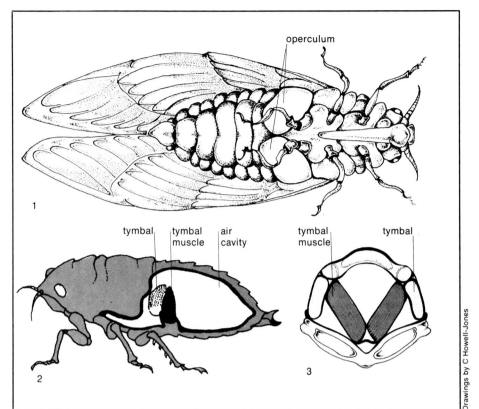

Drawings by C Howell-Jones

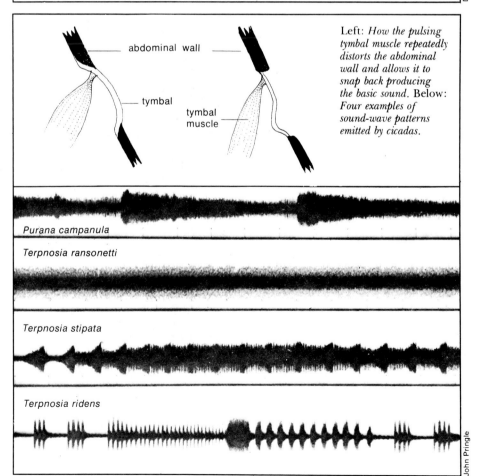

Left: *How the pulsing tymbal muscle repeatedly distorts the abdominal wall and allows it to snap back producing the basic sound.* Below: *Four examples of sound-wave patterns emitted by cicadas.*

Purana campanula

Terpnosia ransonetti

Terpnosia stipata

Terpnosia ridens

John Pringle

Cichlid

The 600 species of cichlid fishes, favourite 'tropicals' of the aquarist, live in rivers and lakes all over Africa, Madagascar and most of South and Central America north to Texas. There are also two species in southern India and Ceylon. Their bodies are flattened from side to side, as in the familiar scalare, the freshwater angelfish, shaped almost like a plate set on edge. In most the head is well developed, the jaws strong, and the lower jaw somewhat jutting. Their colours are attractive and their breeding habits of outstanding interest. This varies in small details from species to species, but for most of them it follows certain general lines.

Colourful courtship

With the onset of breeding conditions, cichlids' colours become heightened, especially in the male. At the same time there is a noticeable difference in behaviour. The male, at such a time, becomes far less sociable and lays claim to a part of the lake or river as his territory. Should another fish, especially one of his own species, swim into this, the breeding male immediately goes into display. His colours become more intense, his fins are fully erected, and the gill-covers are raised. He looks like a galleon going into action, with colours flying, sails set and guns run out.

If the intruder is another male, subsequent action will depend upon whether he is in breeding condition or not. If he is not, he turns and flees, and is chased to the boundary of the territory. But a male in an aggressive mood will return the display. Thereupon the two circle head to tail, each presenting a flank to the other, at the same time beating towards the other's flank with his tail. Very often it goes no farther than this, the fight being broken off by the intruder's flight. It may, however, end in the two contestants seizing each other by the mouth. In any case, the owner of the territory, almost invariably, is victorious. Having your feet on your own property gives a courage and a confidence which the trespasser invariably lacks. So it is with fishes.

Submissive females

The first reaction of an occupying male, when a female fish of his species swims in, is the same as for an intruding male. He displays belligerently. Her behaviour is, however, different. She goes coy, in what has been called an attitude of symbolic inferiority. This does not always save her from attack, but instead of retaliating she accepts the blows, which gradually subside, as the male becomes aware of the presence of a potential mate. In some cichlids there are further preliminaries, the pair seizing each other by the mouth, tugging and twisting in an apparent trial of strength. This may be repeated several times. Usually it ends in a successful mating, although it may end fatally for one or the other.

The choice of partners is only the first stage in a courtship, during which the two

△ *A typical cichlid, the discusfish* Symphysodon *with flattened, plate-shaped body, bright colours, and a slightly jutting lower jaw. Cichlids are adept at guarding their own rigidly defined territories.*

fishes do their best to guard the boundaries of their territory, the male doing most of the displaying or fighting, the female assisting when necessary. Merely defending the territory is only a means to an end, and preparations for spawning go on actively. These include digging pits in the sand with the mouth, and cleaning an area for the reception of the spawn. The spawning site may also be the surface of a stone or, when the cichlids are in an aquarium, part of the glass. Whatever surface is chosen, the two fishes set about cleaning it scrupulously with their mouths.

Cleanliness above all

When the eggs are laid and fertilised, both parents take part in their care. One of them takes up position over the surface on which they are laid, and, stationary, fans the eggs continuously with fins and tail. Every few minutes the parents change over. The fanning probably gives a higher supply of oxygen for efficient development of the eggs, but it may also prevent fungal spores settling and germinating on them. Cleanliness seems to underlie all the attentions given by the cichlids to their eggs. Any that are infertile are eaten, thus reducing the risk of an infection for the rest. At a later stage, too, the eggs are removed from the spawning site to one of the pits dug in the sand. This is done a few at a time, each parent taking the eggs in the mouth to the pit, and as each makes a journey the other stands on guard. Later, by the same laborious process, the eggs are transferred to another of the pits.

When the fry hatch, the parents keep close watch on them. Usually, and especially in the early stages, the fry keep well together, but any that stray are taken in the mouth by one of the parents and returned to the fold. What keeps the young fishes together and within the territory we can only guess. More remarkable, other fishes in the area keep outside the territory.

Invisible wall

The most spectacular aspect of cichlid behaviour is the way a male holding a territory will stop suddenly at its boundary as if bumping his nose against an invisible wall. Although he may swim towards it at speed, there will be the sudden stop at the boundary. Conversely, other fishes beyond the boundary recognize it in like manner and do not normally cross it.

There are two factors involved, both worthy of further consideration. First, the boundary is not only well defined and geometrically regular, but is readily recognized by all concerned. Its position is established by constant fighting before spawning takes place, and it is maintained by the same display of force until the young are old enough to go off on their own. For all that, to appreciate how the other fishes as well as the holders of the territory recognize the boundaries, we have to imagine human properties without fences or hedges and ourselves knowing the boundaries by relatively few landmarks. The second factor is that, for the most part and for most of the time, all fishes in the neighbourhood seem to respect the boundary. Even when invisible, 'good fences make good neighbours'.

△ *Many cichlids hatch their eggs in their mouths, and later may take the young into their mouths.*

▽*Cichlid couples share the job of patrolling their territory, the female assisting as necessary.*

R Apfelbach

L Perkins

Public show ignored

To give an example of this, some years ago in the Aquarium of the London Zoo a pair of black-banded cichlids had 200 babies in a tank 3 ft square and 4½ ft deep. The family occupied a territory at one end. In the same tank were 50 other cichlids, such as firemouths, Brazilians and others. The black-banded cichlids were slightly smaller than the others, yet they might have been enclosed in a glass box. None of the others attempted to enter their territory. Every now and then one of these outsiders would swim towards the well-defined but invisible wall and immediately one of the black-banded cichlids would dart across with fins up, colours temporarily intensified and gill-covers raised. Yet many visitors who looked at the tank saw nothing of this drama.

class	**Osteichthyes**
order	**Perciformes**
family	**Cichlidae**
genera & species	***Cichlasoma nigrofasciatum*** black-banded cichlid ***Geophagus brasiliensis*** *Brazilian cichlid* *others*

Civet

There are 15 species of civet which, with mongooses and genets, make up the Viverridae, a family of carnivores nearly related to the weasel family, on the one hand, and the cat family on the other. Like weasels, civets are long-bodied, with long tails and sharp muzzles but in habits and pattern of coat they resemble the small cats. Civets are sufficiently diverse to make a general account of them difficult. Consequently, those known as binturong, linsang, fossa and palm civets are given special treatment elsewhere in this work. Here we are concerned mainly with the African and Indian, or Oriental, civets which are historically most closely connected with the name.

Originally derived from an Arabic word, the word civet was applied to a scent obtained from the African and Indian species. Later it was applied to the animals themselves, which are sometimes called civet cats.

The African civet, of Africa south of the Sahara, is stout-bodied with short legs, 4 ft total length, with a tail 1½ ft long, ringed black and white, its fur ash-grey, with black spots and stripes. It weighs 15–24 lb. The large Indian civet, of India, Burma and southern China, is about the same size and appearance. The small Indian civet, of southern China to Ceylon and to Bali in the Malayan Archipelago, is similar but smaller. The habits of all three are similar.

Swimmers and climbers

Civets are usually solitary and nocturnal They keep to dense cover, in forests or undergrowth, resting by day, usually in an abandoned burrow, coming out at night to hunt. They can climb and swim well and capture some of their food in water. The voice is a deep growl or a low-pitched cough.

Varied diet

Their food is mainly animal, including insects, crabs, frogs, snakes and birds and their eggs. Vegetable matter is also eaten, mainly fruits, roots and tubers.

Little is known of the life history except that there are usually 2–3 young in a litter, born in a hole in the ground or in dense cover. Civets rarely breed in captivity.

Rare civets

While both the African and Indian civets are common animals, other related species are rare. The fanaloka of Madagascar with the scientific name *Fossa fossa* is not to be confused with another member of the Viverridae, also known as the fossa, and living in Madagascar. It is 2 ft long, of which one third is tail, reddish-grey in colour, with rows of black spots. It is known from a couple of dozen specimens. Owston's civet *Chrotogale owstoni* of southeast Asia, 3 ft long, of which one third is tail, is patterned with dark bands. It is known from 15 specimens in museums. The otter civet *Cynogale*

Solitary night prowler: the ash-grey African civet.

Joe Blossom: NHPA

bennetti of China to Borneo, otter-like in its 2ft body, but with a tail only 8 in. long, has the habits of an otter and takes much the same food: Little more is known about it.

Delicate perfume from rank odour

The main interest shown by man in the African and Indian civets has been in collecting the musk from pods, or glands, near the reproductive organs in both male and female. The musk has the consistency of butter or honey, a clear, yellowish or brownish complex of fats and essential oils, and offensive to the human nose in its concentrated form, but pleasant when diluted. It is accordingly used in some of the best perfumes. In Ethiopia particularly and to a lesser extent elsewhere in Africa civets are kept in captivity and the musk removed from them several times a week. It is 'spooned' out with a specially shaped wooden instrument, each animal yielding less than $\frac{1}{8}$ oz/week. In 1934, 2½ tons were exported from Africa, worth about $120 000 (£50 000). The industry's age is shown by the fact that King Solomon's perfume came from Ethiopia, but synthetic products have

now largely displaced the natural musk in the perfumery trade.

In spite of the long-standing practice of keeping civets in captivity we know, as has already been said, little of their life history. The musk gatherers are no more successful in breeding the animals than zoos have been. The stock from which the musk is drawn is kept up by the capture of wild animals. They are easily trapped, easy to feed because of their wide diet, and are not particularly aggressive.

In Shakespeare's 'Much Ado About Nothing' Claudio is made to remark that when a young man rubs himself with civet 'The sweet youth's in love.' The primary purpose of the animal's scent is to gain for the male the female's favour. Ironically, today women use the perfumes derived from civet for the opposite purpose.

class	**Mammalia**
order	**Carnivora**
family	**Viverridae**
genera & species	***Civettictis civetta*** *African civet* ***Viverra zibetha*** *large Indian civet* ***Viverricula indica*** *small Indian civet*

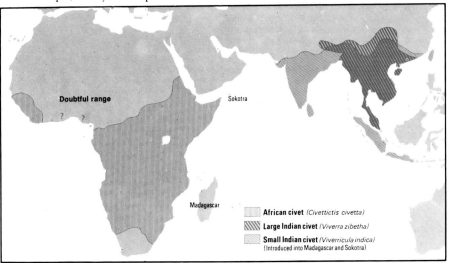

Doubtful range

Sokotra

Madagascar

▦ **African civet** *(Civettictis civetta)*
▨ **Large Indian civet** *(Viverra zibetha)*
▧ **Small Indian civet** *(Viverricula indica)*
(Introduced into Madagascar and Sokotra)

Clam

The word clam means different things to different people. In Scotland 'clam' usually means scallop and in America the name is generally applied to other edible shellfish, such as the hard or round clam or quahog, the great clam, the soft clam, the long clam or sandgaper and the pismo clam. In other places the many freshwater mussels may be called clams or the name may be applied to any mollusc that can 'clam up' inside its two-piece shell. The largest clam of all is the giant clam whose name is not disputed. It is the one to which the main attention will be given here. Others, such as cockles, oysters, shipworms and mussels will be dealt with in later pages. The giant clam and all those mentioned here belong to the group of molluscs known as bivalves or lamellibranchs, and they all have a number of features in common.

Held by its beard

The typical clam's body is enclosed in a shell made of two separate, hinged 'valves'. These are made of calcium carbonate (chalk) secreted by two flaps of tissue immediately beneath them, known as the mantle. The valves can be pulled shut by muscles that run between them. When these muscles relax, the shell is pulled open by a rubbery elastic ligament at the hinge. The animal inside has a foot which may be pushed out and used to creep along burrows, or as in the cockle, make short jumps. Not all bivalves move about, however, and many spend all or a large part of their lives anchored by tough threads spun from a gland at the base of the foot. These threads are known as the byssus.

Dual purpose gills

On either side of the foot, and lying in the space enclosed by the mantle and shell, are the gills. These serve not only for breathing, but also to collect tiny food particles from the water. The gills are typically large double flaps of complex structure through which water is driven by the beating of cilia on their surfaces. In some species water enters the mantle cavity at the front, passes through the gills and leaves at the rear, but in many others water enters and leaves at the hind end through a pair of siphons, which are very long in some species. As food particles reach the gills they become trapped in mucus and this is carried to the mouth, which lies between a pair of ciliated lips. There is nothing that can be regarded as a head. The mouth simply opens into the front part of the body.

The cilia are responsible for a number of tasks, such as drawing water in and driving it out again, and sorting and conveying food particles along well-defined routes. The current of water set up by the gills also brings in oxygen, and when it is pumped out again it takes with it the waste substances of the mollusc itself. In some primitive bivalves these are the two main functions of the water current. The nut shell *Nucula*, for example, does not use its gills for feeding, but collects food particles from the seabed with ciliated tentacles which are really extensions of the lips.

Outsize seashell in the Seychelles: the huge 'jaws' of a long-dead giant clam. They can reach 3–4 ft across, and the whole shellfish may weigh up to ¼ ton. They live in the shallow waters of coral reefs in the Indian and Pacific Oceans.

Alice Brown

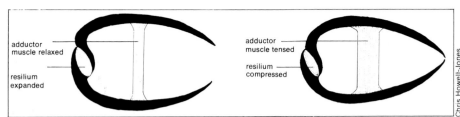

When the adductor muscle relaxes and the
resilium expands, the shells are forced apart.

With resilium compressed and adductor
muscle tensed, the shells are pulled together.

△ Parts of the fleshy mantle of the giant clam
with eyes at intervals along its edges.

▽ Giant clam on the Great Barrier Reef,
showing the mantle and the purple body.

Giant clam: first cloche-gardener

The giant clam *Tridacna* reaches 3 – 4 ft across
and the whole animal may weigh ¼ ton. Its
shells have been made into baptismal fonts
or used in a variety of ways in household
decoration. Giant clams live in the shallow
water of Indo-Pacific coral reefs. The
margins of the shell are corrugated and
when the two valves come together the cor-
rugations fit into each other. Some giant
clams are attached by a byssus in burrows in
the coral, other larger ones are unattached
and held in place by their weight. Giant
clams rest with their hinge downwards and
the margins of the valves directed upwards.
In the colourful edges of the mantle, which
are usually purple with green markings,
live many single-celled algae. Here, they are
exposed to the sun, and can use its energy
to make sugar by photosynthesis, in the
usual manner of plants, at the same time
receiving some nutrients from the host.
Moreover, the light of the sun is concentrated on them by transparent lenses in the
skin. These act like garden cloches, increasing the growth of the algae. The benefit
is mutual: the algae receive some nourish-
ment from the waste products of the clam,
and are given shelter. The clam uses oxygen
given off by the algae and it eats the surplus
'crop'. The algae are contained in special
mobile cells which eventually travel in the
blood to the clam's digestive gland.

Killer myth

The giant clam has been called the killer
clam or man-eating clam. To brand the
clam as man-eating can only be a figure of
speech. Whether it is a killer at all is also
questionable. There are many stories of
pearl divers and others having put a foot
on the clam causing it to snap its shell to,
holding the human victim by the leg until
he drowned. Eminent writers have repeated
the claim that there have been fatalities of
this kind and the *US Diving Manual* has
rated the mollusc dangerous and capable of
trapping arms and legs between the shells.
Certainly the wavy edges of the shell fit into
each other and could grip inexorably.

Roger A Caras, author of *Dangerous to
Man*, could find no records of fatalities.
Accordingly, he canvassed views of experienced biologists, 13 in all, in areas where
giant clams are found. All were of the same
opinion, that there were no authentic cases
on record and that such fatalities were unlikely. Some dubbed the whole thing a myth.

Caras argues, justifiably, that the massive
purple body, seen when the clam is fully
open, is too conspicuous for anyone but the
most unobservant to miss. Moreover, were
someone to tread on the clam, the closing
of the shells would almost certainly be slow,
giving time for the foot to be withdrawn.

phylum	**Mollusca**
class	**Bivalvia**
subclass	**Lamellibranchia**
order	**Eulamellibranchia**
family	**Tridacnidae**
genus & species	*Tridacna gigas* *others*

Classification

In order to classify animals by their relationships and to make international understanding easier zoologists have evolved a far-reaching system of Greek or Latin based names for animals and groupings of animals. This scheme not only gives every different kind of animal its own internationally known name but also fixes its position in relation to the rest of the Animal Kingdom.

The principal categories are as follows. The Animal Kingdom is itself, of course, the largest of them, comprising all animals. The Kingdom is divided first into *phyla*. Although the majority of the commonly known animals fall into one phylum, the Chordata (which includes the vertebrates or back-boned animals), there are very many phyla at the more primitive and widely divergent end of the scale.

The phylum is divided into *classes*: one such is the class Mammalia, containing all the mammals. Classes are again divided into *orders*, distinguishing, for example, the Carnivora from the Primates. After orders come *families*: the apes, for instance, form a family within the order of Primates.

This illustration traces the lion Panthera leo *through its classification, with other examples of genus, family, order, class and phylum.*

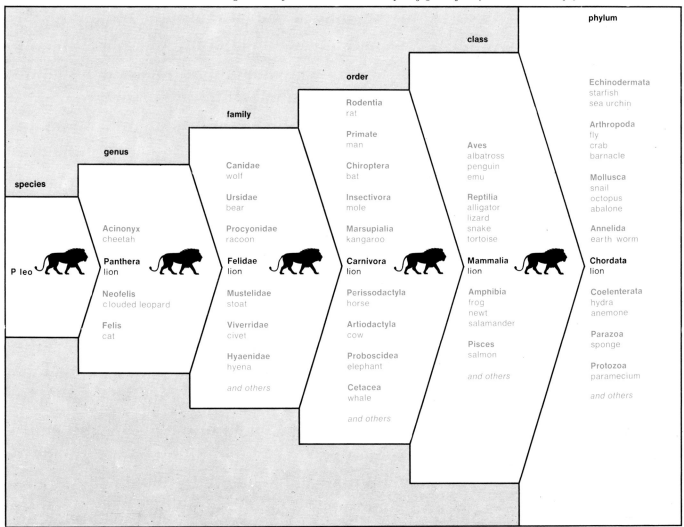

The subdivision of the family is the *genus,* containing very closely related animals; and finally comes the *species,* which defines an animal exactly. The normal scientific way of referring to an animal is by its generic and specific names together. Thus the lion is *Panthera leo: Panthera* is the genus (which also contains the closely related tiger, leopard and jaguar), and *leo,* the specific name (and Latin for lion), narrows the field to the lion alone.

To sum up, let us follow the lion up through the scheme of classification. The genus and species are *Panthera leo*; it belongs to the family Felidae, with all the cat-like animals; the Felidae are part of the order Carnivora, with the other flesh-eating mammals; these join all other mammals in the class Mammalia, which in turn belongs with the birds, fishes and others to the phylum Chordata; and the Chordata belong with all other animals to the Animal Kingdom, as opposed to the plants.

Other subdivisions

Increasing scientific knowledge has made necessary the creation of additional groupings falling between the existing ones. Thus there are subkingdoms, subphyla, subclasses, infraclasses, superorders, suborders, superfamilies, subfamilies, tribes (division of subfamilies), and finally subspecies, or races, which describe local variants of what is basically one species.

Recognition

Species' names can always be recognised because they consist of two words (generic and specific names) printed in italic type — for example *Ursus arctos* (brown bear). For closer identification the sub-specific name may be added, giving for example *Ursus arctos syriacus* (Syrian bear) as distinct from *Ursus arctos arctos* (European brown bear). In cases of repetition the generic name may be designated by its initial, so *U. arctos*.

Other group names are printed in roman type but with capital letters. Family names are recognisable because they always end in -idae: thus Felidae, the cat family, or Canidae, the dog family. Similarly, superfamilies end in -oidea, subfamilies in -inae and tribes in -ini.

For most groups there is no rule for the ending of order names; however, orders of birds always end in -iformes: thus Sphenisciformes, the penguins. Larger groupings than orders offer no means of quick recognition, except that phyla and classes always end in -a — but so may orders and others.

Warning

It must be remembered that names are only names; there is no universal truth about them. Thus classification is always subject to alteration in the light of new scientific discoveries; also, zoologists can disagree about a particular question and divide into two or more camps, each using different terminology. In addition, the same animal may be discovered in different parts of the world and so acquire different names, which take time to sort out.

It must be remembered also that the animal world is in a constant state of change; animals invade new environments and adapt to them, or exploit new food sources, eventually changing enough to be called new species.

An acceptable definition of a species was put forward by the ornithologist Mayr in 1940: 'species are groups of actually or potentially interbreeding populations which are reproductively isolated from other such groups'. Among the 8 500 species of birds, however, there are several scores of species on the point of dividing into new ones (see *Bird Speciation* p 873). Agreement is far from being reached about these alone; the whole Animal Kingdom contains nearly a million species!

For these reasons reference books are not unanimous in their naming of animals in every case: this does not mean that one of them is wrong, but that for some reason the nomenclature is undecided.

King of beasts — a majestic lion Panthera leo *relaxes at the end of the day, catching the last rays of sunlight.*

Robert Grant

Brand names in animal life

Before a manufacturer can market a new product he must give it a brand name, otherwise prospective customers will not know how to ask for it. To avoid confusion the name must be different from any other. A hundred years ago the problem of naming saleable goods was nothing like as acute as it is today, because the number of items was relatively small.

We have an exact parallel with the naming of animals. In the time of the Ancient Greeks little attempt was made to distinguish between animals of the same kind. The word 'eagle', for example, did duty for almost any large bird of prey that flew by day. With the accumulation of knowledge, and with scholars of different nationalities and languages studying animals, there arose a need to say which kind of eagle you were writing about and in a language which everybody could understand. The language problem was solved by using Latin to describe animals, but this was still based on the common names current in various languages. Even with the relatively few animals named by the beginning of the 17th century, at the time when the Royal Society was still to be founded, confusion was already beginning to creep in, and with the naming of more and more animals, the confusion was increasing.

It fell to a Swedish botanist, Carl von Linné (better known by the Latinised form of his name Linnaeus) to come to the rescue with his Binomial System published in his book *Systema Naturae* in 1757. This work went into several different editions, each an improvement of the last, and it is the 10th edition published in 1758 which is now accepted as the standard.

In the *Systema Naturae* a cat is given the Latin name *Felis catus*. 'Cat' may be similar in different languages but there is at least enough difference to make it at times unrecognisable. In French, for example, it is *chat*. In German, however, it is *die Katze*. So we could go on for the rest of the languages. But *Felis catus* is recognisable to all.

The layman may ask why we do not use the ordinary common names. As we see again and again in this Encyclopedia one animal will not only have a different common name in different countries but also in different parts of the English-speaking world. Conversely, one common name may be used for half-a-dozen different kinds of animals in different parts of the world. With one agreed scientific name all this can be avoided, but that name must be in a dead language, otherwise scientists of various countries would never have agreed which language should be used, whether it should be English, French or German.

Often the scientific names are derived from Ancient Greek instead of Latin, but the same principle applies, a dead language is being used. Linnaeus by a stroke of genius presented the scientific world with a master tool at a time when the number of known animals had reached the 'staggering' total of 50 000. He did this just in time to create order out of a growing chaos. We have only to compare this 50 000 with the total of known animals today to appreciate what we owe to Linnaeus. New species are being created at the rate of around 10 000 every year. Estimates of the total of known (that is described) species vary from one million upwards or over 20 times the number known in the days of Linnaeus.

There is another objection often voiced by the layman, and especially by the naturalist, that so often the scientific names are different from one book to another. The explanation is to be found in the history of trying to make the Linnaean system work.

As the list of published names of animal species mounted a further confusion began to creep in. For example, the harvest mouse of Europe had escaped scientific observation, surprisingly, until the 18th century. Then in 1767 Gilbert White found it in Hampshire but he did not publish his observation until 1789, in his *Natural History of Selborne*. He did mention it, however, to Thomas Pennant, who, in his *British Zoology* (1768) referred to it as the less long-tailed fieldmouse. White gave it the name of *Mus minimus* but in the meantime Pallas, a German-born Russian naturalist had also found it and had published a description of it in 1771 as *Mus minutus*. During the next 50 to 60 years this mouse was found in other parts of Europe and given different names by different authors.

This is a good example of what has been happening with very many animals. Eventually an International Commission was set up and it was accepted that in future the law of priority should rule. That is, the scientific name of an animal should be the earliest one given to it. In the case of the harvest mouse this would be *minutus*. Not uncommonly, however, a scientific name would have been widely used perhaps for a century, and printed in a number of books. Then an earlier name would be found, and the law of priority would have to be enforced. But not everybody would become aware of this immediately, and so authors would continue turning out their books, some using one name and some using another for the same animal.

All this is unfortunate, and the possibility of its happening again is still with us. We are reaching something like stability

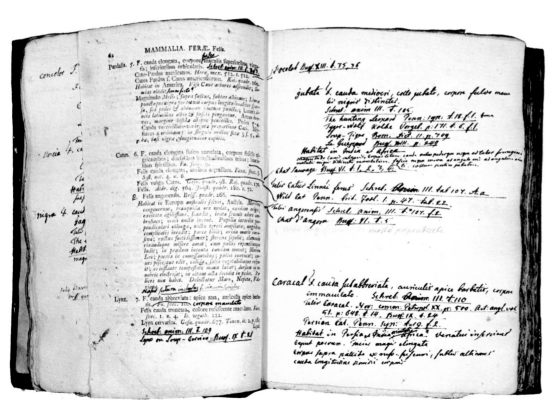

An early edition of Linnaeus' Systema Naturae, *the first published attempt to classify the Animal Kingdom by logical reference to the form of the animals. It was the basis of the binomial system of naming animals. The illustration shows a spread of the book devoted to the cat family. His criteria for the genus* **Felis** *were a rough tongue and retractable claws. He placed this under the 'savage' beasts — those with six sharp primary teeth and single canines (he referred to only one side of one jaw at a time). The handwritten notes on the facing page are additions and corrections by the author's son.*

but it has not yet been achieved. Therefore, in presenting the scientific names of animals in this Encyclopedia we must achieve a temporary stability by following certain authorities. For mammals, we have followed *Mammals of the World* by Ernest P Walker (1964); for the birds, *The New Dictionary of Birds* by Landsborough Thomson (1964).

For the rest we have used the following:
Living Reptiles of the World by Carl P Schmidt and Robert P Inger
Living Amphibians of the World by Doris M Cochran
Living Fishes of the World by Earl S Herald, but with modifications based on a monograph by P H Greenwood and others in the

Bulletin of the American Museum of Natural History volume 131 part 4, 1966.

For the invertebrates we have used mainly *Living Insects of the World*, by Alexander B and Elsie Klots, *Living Invertebrates of the World* by Ralph Buchsbaum and Lorus J Milne, and *A Classification of Living Animals* by Rothschild, 1961.

Harvest mice Mus minutus. *First discovered in 1769 by Gilbert White in Hampshire, England, the same species was found independently by other authors all over Europe in the next 50 to 60 years, and given widely different names. The priority rule gave it its present name.*

Clawed frog

Although sometimes called a toad, the clawed frog belongs to the Aglossa, a group of tongueless frogs. It is larger than a common European frog, usually around 4 in. long, with large females reaching 5 in. The front legs are short and weak, each having 4 long, straight fingers. The back legs, however, are long and very muscular, with large webs between the toes. A clawed frog 3 in. long may have webbed feet 2 in. across. The South African name 'platanna' is derived from 'plathander' meaning flat hands. The three inner toes on each back foot have sharp black claws.

Clawed frogs can change colour to match their background. When this is a contrasting mixture of light and shade, the frogs are mottled, but they can become almost black or a pale buff if placed against uniformly dark or light areas.

A fully aquatic amphibian

Clawed frogs live in tropical and southern Africa, in swamps, streams and ponds. Unlike most other frogs which spend a large part of adult life on land, hiding in damp places and returning to water only to breed, the clawed frog lives in water the whole time. When it does come on land it is clumsy, but in water the strong legs and large webs make it a powerful swimmer. The front legs are also used as paddles, and not held in to the sides as in typical frogs. To escape from enemies, the clawed frogs give a violent forward thrust of the back legs, shooting themselves backwards. The sharp claws are probably used for gripping boulders or plants in fast running streams but they can also be used, by accident or design, as weapons, for a struggling frog can give some nasty scratches with its claws.

When many of the swamps and ponds dry up in summer, the frogs burrow into the mud to remain cool and moist. If the bed, too, dries out, however, the frogs will hop overland in search of permanent water. Otherwise, clawed frogs leave their home waters and move overland only during heavy rain.

Although so wedded to an aquatic life, clawed frogs still need to come to the surface to breathe. Even when inactive, a large frog surfaces every 10 minutes, although it will survive much longer than this if prevented from surfacing. Even common frogs can stay underwater for a long time, getting most of their oxygen through the skin. It is only to be expected, therefore, that the more completely aquatic clawed frog with its very large areas of particularly permeable skin, on the large webs to the feet, can absorb a far greater proportion of dissolved oxygen from the water.

Feeding

Clawed frogs and their relatives do not have the extensible tongue that is used as a kind of sticky harpoon by other frogs. Instead they catch their prey with their hands, digging their thin, pointed fingers in to prevent escape. The food, which consists of carrion, crustaceans, aquatic larvae and small fish, is then crammed into the mouth.

Clawed frogs are full-time amphibians, preferring not to leave the water at all unless forced by summer droughts to move overland. Their muscular hind legs have very large webbed feet, which provide the main drive for powerful swimming.

Jane Burton: Photo Res.

Small particles of food are swept into the mouth by a fanning action of the front feet. Mosquito eggs and larvae are eaten in vast numbers, so that where abundant, clawed frogs benefit men by reducing malaria and other mosquito-borne diseases.

Breeding

At the end of the summer, when the ponds fill and the streams start to run again, the clawed frogs begin to breed. During the breeding season, the males croak morning and evening. Eggs are laid and fertilised after amplexus (the characteristic pick-a-back mating of frogs) the eggs being laid singly on the stems of water plants or on stones. Each egg, and there may be 500–2 000 of them, is 1 mm across and sticky so that it adheres where the female places it.

The tadpoles hatch after about a week, depending on the water temperature, and for another week they hang motionless at the surface of the water. During this time their mouths are closed and they live off the remains of the egg yolk, which has become enclosed in their body. Then they begin to feed on microscopic plants, but instead of scraping these off rocks and the surfaces of larger plants like most tadpoles, they suck water into their mouths and strain off the minute organisms. On each side of the mouth, just under the eyes, the tadpoles have a small tentacle that appears to be sensitive to touch. Quite how it functions is not known. It has been suggested that it helps keep the tadpole out of the mud as it feeds, hanging vertically downwards a short distance from the bottom.

The tadpoles take 2 months or more to turn into adult frogs, during which time they grow legs and lose their tail. They reach sexual maturity in 3–4 years.

Pregnancy testing

The first test for confirming pregnancy at an early stage was devised in 1928. Samples of urine were injected into mice, which were killed and examined 5 days later. If the urine came from a pregnant woman, changes would be found in the ovaries of the mouse, caused by substances called gonadotrophins that are excreted in quantity by pregnant women only. These tests were extremely reliable, but slow, and a year later it was found that tests on rabbits could be completed in a day or two.

Then in 1931 there came a breakthrough. A scientist working in Cape Town found that urine of pregnant women injected into a female clawed frog would cause it to discharge its eggs 5–18 hours later. Here was a test that was not only twice as quick as any other, but it left the animal alive. Each frog could be used many times, so the process of confirming pregnancy became rapid and reliable and, consequently, clawed frogs were exported all over the world.

class	**Amphibia**
order	**Salientia**
family	**Pipidae**
genus & species	*Xenopus laevis*

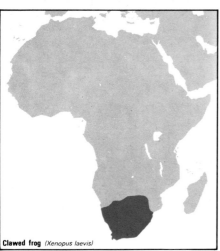

Clawed frog *(Xenopus laevis)*

Top: A closer look at a clawed frog's right foot shows the sharp black claws on the three inner toes. Also visible is the pattern of blood vessels which the frog uses to breathe through the large skin area created by its wide webbed feet. Right: Clawed frogs mating. Larger than the European frog, females can grow to 5 in.

584

Click beetle

If a click beetle falls onto its back it can throw itself into the air making a clicking sound, using a mechanism on the thorax which is peculiar to the family Elateridae. They are small hard-shelled, short-legged, elongated beetles, mainly ¼ in. or so long, which often fly into lighted rooms. Most of the common species are black or dark brown, but some are red, yellow or green. The antennae may be simple or quite elaborately branched. The larvae of many of them feed underground on roots and those of a few species, known as wireworms, are serious crop pests.

Some of the tropical insects called fireflies possess the 'click' mechanism as well as being the most brightly luminous of all insects.

Try, try again

Most click beetles fly actively at night and hide away in the daytime. Apart from the luminosity of some tropical species, their most remarkable feature is the ability to jump with a 'click' when turned on their backs. The way they do this is as follows. The first and second sections of the thorax are hinged, and on the underside of the first there is a spine directed backwards, whose tip rests just over the edge of a cavity in the second. The spine is pressed against this edge, and as the hinge between the two sections moves, it causes the spine to slide until its tip passes over the edge and snaps into the cavity with enough force to jar the whole body of the insect and throw it into the air. If a click beetle is put on its back it can be seen arching its body with the thoracic hinge just before jumping. Naturally the beetle cannot be sure of landing right way up at the first jump, and in fact often fails to do so, but by repeated jumps it sooner or later lands on its feet.

This cumbersome, hit-or-miss method is necessary because the legs of a click beetle are so short that they cannot be used to right the beetle when inverted, so the click mechanism must be of considerable value for this alone. If caught and squeezed, however, the beetles always click repeatedly. This may be no more than a response to being held off balance but it is quite likely that a young, inexperienced bird or lizard, finding and seizing one of these insects, might be so startled by the strength of the clicks that it would drop its prey which would then run away. The mechanism could therefore serve a double purpose.

Arch-enemy of crops

Adult click beetles feed on leaves, mostly at night, and they are also attracted to sweet liquids. Some harmful species are trapped by putting out sweet baits to attract them. The larvae of some click beetles live in rotting wood, but those of the most abundant species, known as wireworms, feed on the roots, bulbs and tubers of plants and also on seeds lying in the ground before germination.

They are elongated, cylindrical, tough-skinned larvae as suggested by the term

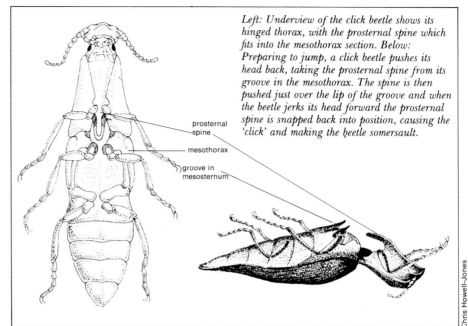

Left: Underview of the click beetle shows its hinged thorax, with the prosternal spine which fits into the mesothorax section. Below: Preparing to jump, a click beetle pushes its head back, taking the prosternal spine from its groove in the mesothorax. The spine is then pushed just over the lip of the groove and when the beetle jerks its head forward the prosternal spine is snapped back into position, causing the 'click' and making the beetle somersault.

prosternal spine

mesothorax

groove in mesosternum

Chris Howell-Jones

△ Adult click beetles are about ¼ in. long.

▽ Younger generation: the 'wireworm' larva.

Stephen Dalton: NHPA

GE Hyde

'wireworm', usually yellow in colour, and are among the most serious of all insect pests. Most cultivated crops are attacked, but especially cereals and potatoes.

Menace for 6 years

The eggs are laid in the soil and the larvae develop slowly, taking 2–6 years to reach full growth. In the commonest British wireworm *Agriotes obscurus* the larval life duration is probably 5 years. Only a few weeks are spent as a pupa, but the adults may live for 10 months or a year, overwintering in the soil in temperate and cold climates.

Coping with wireworms

Wireworms, larvae of click beetles of the genera *Agriotes* and *Athous*, are serious agricultural pests. In land that is already cultivated, some measure of control can be achieved by getting rid of weeds (which support the wireworms between crops) frequent working of the soil and careful use of insecticides, but they are among the most difficult to destroy of all insects harmful to agriculture.

When grassland is ploughed it is usual for an economic entomologist to sample the soil and determine the approximate number of wireworms present in it per acre. If the figure exceeds a million, no crop stands much chance of success. Over 600 000 are a serious threat to most crops on light soil, but on heavy soil peas can be planted and also barley, the least susceptible of the cereals. For all crops except potatoes, 300–600 thousand is fairly safe, and the farmer whose ploughed grassland contains less than 300 000 wireworms/acre must consider himself fortunate.

phylum	**Arthropoda**
class	**Insecta**
order	**Coleoptera**
family	**Elateridae**
genus & species	*Agriotes obscurus* others

B Pengilley

In the water with spiny dorsal fin lowered. It 'walks' on land by digging the spines of the gill covers into the ground, using the pectoral fins as props and pushing with its tail.

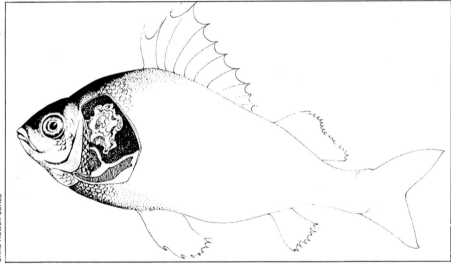

Chris Howell-Jones

Cutaway diagram of the gill cavity, showing the large air-breathing rosette section.

Climbing perch

Although long familiar to scientists under the name Anabas scandens *the name of this fish is now* Anabas testudineus. *It is 9 in. long, perch-like, grey-green to greyish-silver with brown fins, and there is a dark patch behind each gill-cover and another at the base of the tailfin. Climbing perch extend across southern and southeast Asia, from India and Ceylon to the Philippines.*

Overland wanderer

Little would have been heard of this ordinary looking fish but for its habit of travelling overland to find a fresh pond when its home water is drying up. It does this using the gill-covers, pectoral fins and tail. The gill-covers have spines on their hind margins which are dug into the ground with a side-to-side rocking motion. The pectoral fins are used as props to help the forward thrust from the tail-end. It is half

a wriggle and half a seal lollop enabling the fish to travel at about 200 yd an hour.

The ability to breathe out of water is due to a large gill cavity, divided into two compartments. The smaller and lower of these contains the normal gills. The larger upper part contains a rosette of concentrically arranged plates with wavy edges, the whole richly supplied with a network of fine blood-vessels. In fact, the rosette works like a piece of lung. Air is swallowed and passes by an opening on either side of the throat into the rosette chambers, the opening being controlled by a valve. The spent air leaves through the gills' exit, in the usual way.

A drowning fish

It is not only while the fish is out of water that this accessory breathing apparatus is used. Like the true lungfishes, and others that have lungs or lung-like organs, the climbing perch can live in water low in oxygen—water polluted and foul from rotting vegetation. In such water it can rise to the surface and gulp air. Indeed, the

climbing perch is one of several fishes which drown if held under water.

Although the overland speed of the climbing perch is slow, the fish can stay out of water for a long time. The people of India and Malaya carry them for days on end in moistened clay pots. It is one way of ensuring a supply of fresh fish.

There is no difficulty in catching climbing perch in the right season. At the beginning of the dry season the fish burrows into mud and goes into a resting stage, like the well-known lungfishes. At other times, and usually in the early morning or during a rainstorm, the fishes travel over the ground in troops. Climbing perch are tolerant of sudden temperature changes, and feeding offers few problems since they take a wide variety of animal and plant food.

Casual parents

It is surprising, in view of their wide diet, that climbing perch do not eat their young, as so many freshwater fishes are prone to do, after nursing them through early infancy. The female climbing perch lays her eggs at random; these float to the surface and the parents show no further interest in them. The eggs hatch in a day or so.

End of a legend

The western world first learned of the existence of the climbing perch in 1797, when Lieutenant Daldorf of the Danish East India Company, stationed at Tranquebar, wrote a memoir on it. In this he pointed out that the local legend was that the fish climbed palm trees and sucked their juices. Daldorf confirmed the story by saying he himself had found one in a slit in the bark of a palm growing near a pond.

For nearly 250 years the perch was called 'climbing' and nobody questioned it. Possibly this was due to two facts that appeared to bear out the fish's reputation. One was that the perch will climb the trunk of a tree leaning well over, just as the marine fishes known as mud-skippers will. The other fact is that the perch is sometimes found well up a tree, in a crotch or a fork or even in a slit in the bark, as Lt Daldorf found his.

Then, in 1927, Dr BK Das, the Indian expert on fishes, discovered that perch in trees do not get there under their own steam. When troops of perch are travelling in search of fresh ponds crows and kites swoop and carry some of them off, and they park their catch in various places, including trees. The perch can live for days out of water so it must often have happened that people have found live perch high up in trees. What more natural than to draw the obvious conclusion, which fooled us for 250 years until Dr Das took a closer look?

Now it is becoming fashionable among students of fishes to call it a walking perch —but even this is an exaggeration.

class	**Osteichthyes**
order	**Perciformes**
family	**Anabantidae**
genus & species	***Anabas testudineus***

Clothes moths are secretive and fly little, preferring to creep for shelter into cracks and folds. This mounted specimen shows its soft feathery wings.

Clothes moth

Three species of small moths whose larvae damage furs and woollen fabrics by feeding on them are called clothes moths. All three belong to the family Tinaeidae.
Common clothes moth Tineola bisselliella. *Length from head to wing-tips about 6 – 8 mm. Forewings (the part seen when the moth is at rest) pale buff or golden with a distinct metallic sheen and with no spots or markings. The larva is creamy-white with a brown head and about 10 mm long when fully grown. The brown pupa is enclosed in a cocoon from which it protrudes after hatching.*
Case-bearing clothes moth Tinaea pellionella. *Similar in appearance to the common clothes moth, but rather darker and duller and with three dark spots on each wing. The larva is more easily distinguished by its habit of making a case of silk and fibre which it drags about*

in the same way as the larva of a caddisfly. The pupa is formed inside the case, which then serves as a cocoon.
White-tip clothes moth Trichophaga tapetzella. *Larger than the other two clothes moths, length from 8 to over 10 mm. The forewings are dark coloured with the basal third white and the front of the head covered with white hairs. The insect at rest, therefore, appears dark on its hinder two-thirds and white in front. It infests coarser materials than the other two, and is, therefore, sometimes called the tapestry moth.*

Two other species, commonly known as house moths, are often encountered in houses, and their larvae feed on any organic matter that is slightly damp – neglected scraps of food, leather, wool and feathers – but they are seldom found infesting fabrics stored in dry conditions. Both belong to the family Oecophoridae.
Brown house moth Hofmannophila pseudospretella *is brown speckled*

with dark flecks, the female (over 14 mm long) much larger than the male (8 – 9 mm).
White-shouldered house moth
Endrosis sarcitrella *is mottled greyish-brown with the head and front of the thorax white, and is much smaller than the other species, being more comparable with the clothes moths in size. Here again the female is larger (about 10 mm).*

Hard to keep out

Clothes moths are secretive, much more inclined to run and hide in a fold or crevice than to fly. Most of those seen flying are males, or females that have laid all their eggs. They can squeeze through very narrow crevices and will make their way into almost any cupboard or chest of drawers, however well made.

Clothes moth larvae can live on clean wool or fur, but greatly prefer those garments that are soiled by body excretions or by food dropped on them. They bite through and scatter far more fibres than they eat, which accounts for the great amount of damage that such small creatures can do.

Time/temperature formula

The female common clothes moth lays from 50–100 eggs which hatch in a week in very warm conditions (27°–32°C/80°–90°F) but take 3 weeks or more at 16°C/60°F. The rate at which the larvae grow varies widely with the availability of food. On raw wool or rabbit fur they may become moths in 3 or 4 months, but they often take a year to reach maturity on manufactured cloth, and a period of as much as 4 years has been recorded for their development. The adult moths live from 2–3 weeks.

Details of the breeding of the other species are less well known but appear to be generally similar.

Enemies and means of control

A small parasitic chalcid wasp *Spathius exarator* lays its eggs in the larvae of clothes moths, and the larvae of the window fly *Scenopinus fenestralis* prey on the larvae of both clothes moths and house moths.

The chief enemies of clothes moths are moth-proofing, dry-cleaning and synthetic fabrics, combined with constantly improving standards of hygiene in homes. If woollens are kept scrupulously clean and carpets regularly cleaned with a sweeper or vacuum cleaner they are not likely to become infested. Parts of carpets under heavy furniture should be sprayed every 6 months with a persistent insecticide. Bright light and good ventilation destroy the moths in all their stages, and stored blankets should be regularly aired out of doors on sunny days. Sudden changes of temperature also kill the insects, a fact that lends point to the cold storage of furs in summer.

Clothes moths are becoming rarer, so that even in conditions favourable for them, infestation is less general than it used to be.

Before the days of cloth

Clothes moths are now very seldom found in the 'wild' state, but, of course, they must have existed before the coming of civilised man, probably before man had evolved as a species at all. At that time they must have lived in such places as old birds' nests and the lairs of carnivorous animals. There the larvae probably fed on the feathers and hair used by the birds for their nests and on scraps of skin discarded by the animals. Early in his development, man behaved very much like a carnivorous animal, and later he took to using skins as clothing. Later still he learned to spin and weave wool. Widespread regard to cleanliness is a very recent feature in human development and even now is far from universal. Clothes moths have probably lived with man during the whole of his evolutionary development and, although they are on the wane, they will be with us in small numbers at least for some time to come.

class	**Insecta**
order	**Lepidoptera**
family	**Tinaeidae, Oecophoridae**
genera	***Tineola, Hofmannophila, Endrosis***

Yves Lanceau

Klaus Paysan

△ *Examining the menu; dry cleaners are deadly enemies of the moth.*
◁ *The face of innocence: European apple-tree moth alights on a flower.*
▽ *Aftermath: woollen fabric after attacks by clothes moth larvae.*

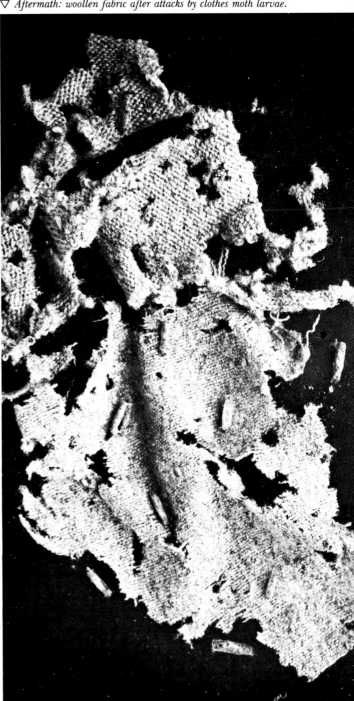

L Hugh Newman: NHPA

Coalfish

A member of the cod family, up to 3½ ft long, characterised by the dark colour of its back, the coalfish was given its name about the year 1600, because of its black colouring, but 30 years later was given the alternative name of saithe. In North America it is known as pollock or pollack.

Contrasting with the dark colour of the body, the lateral line is white. The lower jaw projects forwards beyond the tip of the upper jaw. There are 3 dorsal and 2 anal fins and the pelvics are well forward, on the throat. There is a short barbel on the chin.

Fried cod in disguise

Coalfish was extensively fished and exported from Britain at the beginning of this century, because, in contrast with its popularity in Norway, it was not favoured as a food-fish. Today, however, it is widely used in fried fish shops, whose patrons find it highly palatable.

The coalfish ranges from the Arctic to the Mediterranean. The adult moves about over considerable distances and the fry are carried hundreds of miles by currents. So although the spawning grounds are restricted the mature fishes are well spread out.

Devouring their cousins

The members of the cod family are voracious feeders, smaller fishes being an important item in their diet. Ironically, the coalfish feed on the fry of a near relative, the Atlantic cod. They surround a shoal of fry on all sides, driving them into a dense mass. Then, by a sudden manoeuvre, they drive the fry upwards towards the surface, the coalfishes attacking from below while seabirds, always on the watch for anything unusual in the water below, gather overhead, wheeling and screaming, to attack the fry from above.

The coalfish feeds on other, smaller fishes as well as small crustaceans, such as amphipods. As with so many predatory fishes it swallows its food whole and takes 5—6 days to digest a fish meal, the bones being softened towards the end of this period. A crab swallowed whole will be digested in a similar period but its skeleton, being on the outside, becomes softened first. The smaller crustaceans, such as amphipods, are digested in 3—3½ days.

Coalfishes' infancy

The main spawning grounds of the coalfish are off the west coasts of the British Isles, in the North Sea and off Norway. The eggs are laid during January to May, each egg being 1 mm diameter and surrounded by a transparent membrane within which is a tiny globule of oil that gives it buoyancy. So although the eggs are laid at depths of 200—600 ft they quickly rise to the surface and float there. Inside the egg-membrane and forming part of the egg is a supply of yolk on which the embryo develops. Each of the newly-hatched fry carries a yolksac on its underside, the contents of which

DP Wilson

△ *The coalfish: twin fins on the belly, three on the back, slightly jutting lower jaw, and a small barbel on the chin. On the rocks at the back of this aquarium tank are brittlestars.*

G Mundey

▽ *A shoal of coalfish in east Scottish waters. They feed voraciously on their small relatives.*

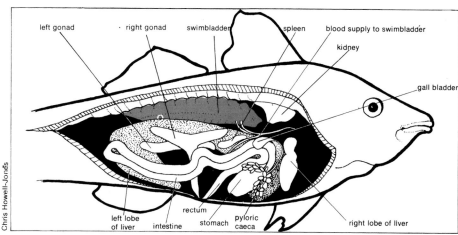

△ *Diagram of coalfish dissection to show relative position of swimbladder.*

nourish it during the early days of life. The yolksac is larger than the baby coalfish and more buoyant, so the fry float upside-down at the surface. As the yolk becomes used and the yolksac shrinks the baby fish slowly turns the right way up. It is finally ready, in 6–9 days from hatching, to swim deeper and start feeding itself, on very small crustaceans.

The rate at which the eggs hatch depends on the temperature of the water. With water up to 10°C/49°F 6 days are needed; at 6°C/43°F incubation takes 9 days. The rate at which the yolksac disappears also depends on temperature, as does later growth. Consequently coalfishes in the southern part of the range grow more quickly than those farther north.

Coalfishes are known to have lived for 14 years.

Internal lifebelt

The coalfish, in common with other members of the cod family, has a swimbladder. This is an elongated silvery bag readily seen when the body of the fish is opened

up. It lies just under the backbone among the organs of the digestive system. From this maw or sound, as it is also called, isinglass is made. It is a sort of gelatine, once used for preserving eggs and for clarifying beers and wines, and for a variety of other purposes.

Many fishes, both freshwater and marine, have a swimbladder. It is an outgrowth of the gullet and probably first arose as an organ of breathing. In most species it now acts as a hydrostatic organ. Usually in freshwater fishes it is connected by a duct with the gullet. In most marine fishes this duct has been lost and the swimbladder is separated from the gullet.

The walls of the swimbladder are richly supplied with blood-vessels and in marine fishes these are concentrated to form a gas gland capable of giving out a mixture of oxygen and nitrogen in roughly the proportions they exist in air. Another knot of blood-vessels, known as the oval, can absorb these gases. Using these a fish can inflate or deflate the bladder, adjusting the volume to keep the density of its body as a whole equal to that of the surrounding water. As it goes deeper and the pressure on the body increases the swimbladder must be inflated to compensate for this. The reverse takes place as it rises.

Those marine fishes lacking a swimbladder must keep swimming all the time or they sink. Those with one can float and therefore rest by adjusting the bladder according to the depth. It is a sort of adjustable Mae West worn internally, or, better still, can be compared with the buoyancy tanks of a submarine.

There is one disadvantage to this internal lifebelt. A fish with a swimbladder may not dive quickly nor surface quickly from a depth. What would happen if it did is illustrated by the fate of deep sea fishes brought quickly to the surface in a net. They arrive at the surface with the stomach sticking out of the mouth, forced out by the pressure from the swimbladder, which the fish has not had time to deflate.

salmon

'primitive' bony fish swimbladder opening to pharynx

pharynx

cod

'advanced' bony fish swimbladder as hydrostatic organ opening to pharynx lost

bowfin

'primitive' air-breathing fishes opening retained and swimbladder developed as 'lungs'

lungfish

bichir

class	**Osteichthyes**
order	**Gadiformes**
family	**Gadidae**
genus & species	***Gadus virens***

Coati

The coati is a small carnivorous mammal related to the raccoon, cacomistle and cat-bear. The head and body measure 1½–2 ft long. The ears are small and the forehead flat, running down to a long, mobile snout that extends beyond the jaw. The black nose at the tip is moist which helps give the coati an excellent sense of smell. The general colour is reddish-brown to black, with yellowish-brown underparts and black and grey markings on the face. The tail is up to 2½ ft long and is banded. It is generally held vertically with the tip curled over.

The three species of coati are found in the forests of South and Central America. They are also found in the southwestern parts of the United States, in Arizona, New Mexico and Texas and here they are extending their range northwards.

◁ *An inquisitive coati standing on its hind legs to get a better view.*

Social forest dweller

Young coatis and the females live in bands of up to 20. The males lead a solitary life outside the breeding season. Each band has a home range, the borders of which overlap with those of other bands, but they rarely meet because they tend to stay near the centres of the ranges. When they do meet, there is usually some threatening and arguing but rarely any fighting. The band forages together, retiring just after sunset to a favoured tree where the coatis remain until sunrise. They sleep curled up with their tails over their faces, in nests of twigs and creepers placed in a fork or on a mat of branches. Several coatis may share a nest. There is no fixed hierarchy, or 'peck order', and there is very little aggression between members of a band. Neither is there any system of sentinels to keep guard while the band is feeding.

Although very active throughout the day, the coatis being very inquisitive, there are periods of rest, when the members of a band will groom themselves. This is an all engrossing habit and one was seen to scratch so hard with her forepaws that she rolled off a log and lay on the ground still scratching. Coatis also groom each other. Sitting head-to-tail they work over each other's bodies, gently nibbling with their teeth. Not only will this keep them clear of parasites, it probably strengthens the bonds between the individuals in the group. While they are out foraging, the band may get split up, but before long the parties will search for each other, with chittering calls, the laggards running to catch up and the others doubling back to find them.

When travelling through the forests coatis walk or gallop with fore- and hindfeet working together, presenting an amusing sight as the band bounds over the ground with tails held high. They also adopt two gaits in climbing, either ascending hand-over-hand or galloping up wide trunks with forefeet and hindfeet clutching the bark together. To descend, they come down head-first with their hindfeet held backwards, like a squirrel, but they are not so completely at home in the trees as a squirrel or pine marten. They will jump from branch

▽ *A troop of coatis. Outside the breeding season the males are solitary, but the females and young live in bands of up to 20, sharing nests to sleep and taking turns to groom each other.*

Phillippa Scott

to branch, but not over any great distance, and they seem to fall quite often, although they land without hurting themselves.

Foraging in the forest

Coatis forage both in the leaf litter on the forest floor and up the trees. On the ground they run about, sniffing to locate any small animals hidden underground or in rotten logs. Here many kinds of invertebrate can be snapped up, including millipedes, earthworms, termites, snails and tarantulas. Lizards and mice are chased when flushed and dug out of their holes, as are land crabs and caecilians. The coatis are very persistent once they have discovered some small animal's lair, digging down after it like a dog. They have been seen to spend half an hour digging out lizards, burrowing so far down that their bodies have disappeared from sight. Land crabs are dealt with by deftly flicking them into the open and ripping off their claws. If their prey escapes and bolts, the whole band will set off in pursuit of it.

leaves the band and makes a nest in a tree. The 2—6 young are born in the nest and remain there for 5 weeks, by which time they can run and climb well enough to keep up with their mother when she rejoins the band.

The mother sits to suckle her babies

The babies are suckled by their mother who is in a sitting position, with her infants lying on their sides, holding on with their forepaws. Sometimes the young coatis become too adventurous and have to be rescued from a precarious position among the branches by their mother, who carries them in her mouth.

After the female rejoins the band the young stay with her, only gradually becoming more independent. The young males leave the band when they become sexually mature at 2 years.

The longevity of the bandicoot in captivity is between 9 and 15 years. A red coati lived for 14 years, 9 months, 1 day in the Philadelphia Zoological Gardens.

life with the segregation of the sexes. This is more usual in the hoofed animals, but in the bighorns, for instance, the males flock together outside the breeding season, whereas the male coatis are strictly solitary. Each male has its own range and is aggressive towards any other male it should meet. The bands are also aggressive to the males, driving them away by threats or actual attacks. One adult female can send a male packing and sometimes the whole band will descend on him and drag him down. Even the immature males will face up unafraid to the old males because they have the support of the rest of the band.

class	**Mammalia**
order	**Carnivora**
family	**Procyonidae**
genus & species	*Nasua nasua* *N. nelsoni* *N. narica*

On the track of a meal. Coatis are inveterate diggers—especially when hunting lizards—and will often dig themselves underground.

Klaus Paysan

In the Amazon River jungle. As well as foraging in the leaf litter on the jungle floor, coatis readily climb for their food.

Meston

Once the prey is caught it is killed either by being bitten in the neck in the case of lizards and rodents, or by being rolled under the front paws until well mangled. This may be to crush the shell or wipe off hairs, stings and so on.

Coatis eat fruits such as wild bananas, figs, mangoes and papayas, either eating the fallen fruit or climbing the trees to pluck it. Sometimes a band splits up, one part waiting under the trees to pick up fruit dropped by the others.

Young reared in nests

Mating takes place during the dry season. During this time the bands of females and juveniles are joined by the males, who are aggressive towards each other, each male jealously guarding his own band, although additional males are also discouraged by the females. The male sleeps and grooms with the band. Gestation lasts 10 or 11 weeks and just before the litter is due, the female

Rogue males

'Coati' is derived from South American Indian words 'cua' (belt) and 'tim' (nose), but why they should be called 'beltnoses' is obscure. The Latin name *Nasua* or 'nosy one' is more appropriate, when one considers the way they thrust their long snouts through leaf litter and down holes in search of food. Another English vernacular name is coatimundi, but this should refer specifically to the lone males, for the inhabitants of Central and South America thought that there were two kinds of animal—the coati living in bands, and the coatimundi, leading a solitary life. It also has native names of 'pisote', or 'pisote solo' in Spanish American, the latter referring to the solitary animal. Before anyone had studied the animal this distinction was accepted by zoologists and two species were named: *Nasua sociabilis* and *Nasua solitaria*.

Coatis certainly have an unusual social

Coati

///// *Nasua narica*

▓▓ *Nasua nasua*

Cobra

Immortalised in Kipling's story of the hardy mongoose Rikki-Tikki-Tavi, the true cobras of the genus Naja, *from the Sanskrit word 'naga' for snake, are medium-sized snakes. Several species average 6 or 7 ft. The Indian cobra has a dark body encircled by a series of light rings, and like all cobras, it has the characteristic hood behind the neck. The hood is flattened horizontally by long, movable ribs being swung out to stretch the loose skin of the neck, rather like the ribs of an umbrella stretching out the fabric. The cobra rears up and expands the hood when frightened or excited, and, in the Indian cobra, this displays the distinctive spectacled pattern as the scales slide apart. The pattern is on the back of the hood but it can be seen from the front as the stretched skin is translucent.*

Another well-known species is the its range, the markings vary. In the west the hood has the typical 'spectacle' markings, but towards the eastern side of India a single ring-like marking becomes more common, while in the Kashmir and Caspian region the hood is marked with black transverse bars.

There are four species in Africa, the black-and-white cobra, the Cape cobra, the spitting cobra and the Egyptian cobra, which is also found in Asia.

Some cobras, such as the Egyptian cobra, are diurnal, others nocturnal like the Indian cobra, retiring by day to a favoured shelter in a burrow or under rocks. Some are found only near water.

Inoculating nerve-poisons

The cobra's venom is secreted from glands which lie just behind the eyes. It runs down ducts to the fangs that grow from the front of the upper jaw. Each fang has a canal along the front edge, and in some species the sides of the canal fold over to form a

with weak hearts, are most likely to succumb. The Indian cobra is regarded by many experts as being one of the most dangerous snakes and death has been recorded as little as 15 minutes after the bite. Figures of 10 000 deaths a year have been given for India, which represents 1 in 30 000 of the population. Snakebite is so common in Asia and Africa because so many of the country people go about barefooted. Some cobras, notably the spitting cobra, of Africa, defend themselves by spitting venom over a distance of up to 12 ft. They aim for the face and the venom causes great pain and temporary blindness if it gets in the eyes.

Cobra venom has a different effect on the body than that of vipers which acts principally on the blood system, destroying tissues. Some tissue damage is done by cobra venom causing swelling and haemorrhage, but the principal ingredients are neurotoxins acting on the nervous system causing paralysis, nausea, difficulty in breathing and, perhaps, eventually death through heart and breathing failure.

One of the four African species, the Cape cobra eats snakes as well as rodents, and is not averse to cannibalism.

Indian cobra, with its distinctive pattern. A cobra's hood works like an umbrella, with long, flexible ribs spreading the thin skin.

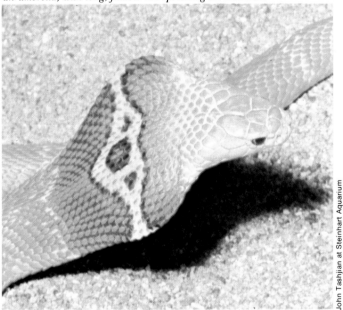

John Tashjian at Fort Worth Zoo

John Tashjian at Steinhart Aquarium

Egyptian cobra, depicted on Ancient Egyptian headdresses rearing up with its hood inflated, and presumed to have been the instrument of Cleopatra's suicide (see Asp, p. 233). Average length of adults is 5½–6 ft and there are reports of their reaching 10 ft, although the longest reliable measurement is just over 7 ft. The body is yellowish to almost black, the lighter forms often having darker spots.

Cobras are found in Africa and Asia, although fossils have been found in Europe, presumably dating from a time when the climate was warmer. There are two or four species in Asia, the number depending on different authorities' methods of classification. One of these is the Indian cobra that is found from the Caspian across Asia, south of the Himalayas to southern China and the Philippines, and south to Bali in Indonesia. Throughout

hollow tube like a hypodermic needle, so resembling the hollow fangs of vipers. The cobra strikes upwards, with the snout curled back so that the fangs protrude. As soon as they pierce the victim's flesh, venom is squirted down the fangs by muscles that squeeze the venom gland. When a very aggressive cobra tightens these muscles too early venom dribbles from its mouth.

Cobras' fangs are fairly short, but after it has struck the snake hangs on, chewing at the wound and injecting large quantities of venom. The seriousness of the bite depends very much on how long the cobra is allowed to chew. If it is struck off immediately, the bite will probably not be too serious. It is always difficult to assess the dangers of snake bite. Even where good medical records are kept, some of the less severe cases will probably not be reported, and the severity depends so much on the condition of the victim. Young and old people and those who are sick, especially

Rat-catching snakes

Cobras eat mainly rodents, coming into homes after rats, which is a cause of many accidents. Frogs, toads and birds are also eaten, the cobras climbing trees to plunder nests. The Egyptian cobra often raids poultry runs. The Cape cobra often eats snakes, including its fellows, and the black-and-white cobra is reported to hunt fish. When food is short they will eat grasshoppers and other large insects.

Cobras' mating dance

Before mating, the pair 'dance', raising their heads a foot or more off the ground and weaving to and fro. This may continue for an hour before mating takes place, when the male presses his cloaca to the female's and ripples run through his body from tail to head.

The Cape cobra mates between September and October and the eggs are laid a month later. These dates vary through the cobras' range as they mate and lay eggs at the season most likely to provide abundant food for the young. Eggs number 8 – 20, and are laid in a hole in the ground or in a tree. The female may stand guard and during the breeding period is irritable and aggressive. She is liable to attack without provocation with dire results for passers-by if her nest is near a footpath. Newly-hatched cobras measure about 10 in.

Enemies

The traditional enemies of cobras are the mongooses, but genets also attack them. The mongoose's tactics are to leap backwards and forwards, around the cobra, keeping it continually on the alert until it tires and cannot hold its body raised in striking position. The mongoose is pro-tected by the speed of its movements and by being very resistant to the cobra's venom. Mongooses do not always win, however. It has been suggested that the inflated hood serves as a protection, making it difficult for any enemy to bite the cobra's neck. Cobras also sham dead, going limp until danger passes.

Snake-charmer's bluff

Cobras, especially the Indian and Egyptian species, are the favourite performers in the snake-charmer's act. It is perhaps fairly common knowledge now that the snakes are not reacting to the music but to the rhythmic movements of the charmer. The pipe is merely a stage prop, and is not used by all performers, because snakes are deaf, or, in other words, they cannot perceive airborne vibrations. They have no eardrum that in most other terrestrial animals vibrates in time to the airborne waves, and they do not have the systems of bones and ducts that convey the vibrations from the eardrum to the sense cells of the inner ear. They can, however, detect vibrations through the earth.

The explanation of the cobras' dance is that the basket is suddenly opened, exposing the snakes to the glare of daylight. Half-blinded and somewhat shocked, they rear up in the defensive position with hoods inflated. Their attention is caught by the first moving object they see, which is the swaying snake-charmer, whose actions they follow.

Part of the act consists of the cobras being handled and even kissed on the head. This

The legendary 'asp' or Egyptian cobra grows to a length of nearly 6 ft; and length for length it is much heavier than the Indian cobra.

is not such a dare-devil act of bravado as it may seem for it is said that cobras cannot strike accurately in the full light of day, and, anyway, their fangs will have been drawn or their lips sewn up. If this has not been done, the chances are that the charmer is immune to their venom.

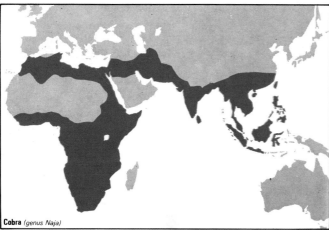

Cobra (genus Naja)

class	**Reptilia**
order	**Squamata**
suborder	**Serpentes**
family	**Elapidae**
genus & species	*Naja naja* Indian cobra *N. haje* Egyptian cobra *N. nivea* Cape cobra *N. nigricollis* spitting cobra *N. melanoleuca* black-and-white cobra *others*